Enough = they ain't right to litter a for strike

+ they ain't needed to more enough damage to this country in the event of a strike

An Inquiry into ENOUGHNESS

preceding page
LIE-DOWN IN LONDON
Ban-the-bomb demonstrators
lie in protest before
a government building.

BOOKS BY DANIEL LANG

Early Tales of the Atomic Age
Man in the Thick Lead Suit
From Hiroshima to the Moon
An Inquiry into Enoughness

Children's Book:
A Summer's Duckling

An Inquiry into ENOUGHNESS

Of Bombs and Men and Staying Alive

By Daniel Lang

McGraw-Hill Book Company
New York Toronto London

Library of Congress Catalog
Card Number: 65-17652

FIRST EDITION

36236

TO HELEN AND FRANK

With the exception of the foreword,
the contents of this book
originally appeared in *The New Yorker*
in slightly different form.
My thanks are extended
to William Knapp for his valuable help
in its preparation.
D.L.

Contents

Foreword

Like other books of mine, *An Inquiry into Enoughness* is probably destined to be placed on the Science and Technology shelf in bookshops and libraries. I have no particular objection, but the buyer should beware that there are absolutely no tables of atomic weights or mathematical equations to be found in these pages (and this is not said as a boast). If there is a theme to the disparate contents of this book, it is that we are trying to stay alive. It takes individuals to do this, just as it takes individuals to die, and this point, in my opinion, is often lost on us. Many of us carry around only the Big Picture, even though our faces and those of our children are missing from it. We tend to think in terms of ever more powerful bombs, all of them abstrusely named—nuclear, thermonuclear, cobalt, neutron. "Clean" bombs, "dirty" bombs, intercontinental missiles, space satellites tipped with warheads—these are the images that spin in our minds when we feel up to contemplating the state of the world. It all seems beyond our grasp, as though, unknowing, we had stumbled past some point of no return. So formidable is the swirl of modern weaponry that few of us dare to stop and wonder whether our lives—our personal lives—are being helped or hurt by what is going on. The question appears bold and out of order and unfairly sweeping; one might just as well ask how the human condition is coming along. A subtle disowning of our own creations is at work, as though we ordinary mortals couldn't possibly have anything to do with such matters. They are unreal to us, and our impulse is to surrender to the ways of magic, like savages staring at lightning.

The possibility that the reasoned, calculated works of our scientific age are being mistaken for magic is, of course, a huge irony. The last guise in which most scientists care to appear is that of magicians. They know that this can only make for a public, untutored and gaping, whose mesmerization is as likely to end in boos as in cheers. This sort of audience, as they also know, is hardly congenial to science, which thrives in an environment of intelligence. Indeed, intelligence is its stock in trade; without it, the scientific method would be nothing. But science and its method transcend the laboratory, as scientists themselves—the rulers of the laboratory—constantly seek to impress on laymen like myself. How often they have remarked, publicly and privately, that science is not all oscilloscopes and electron microscopes. One of the scientists in this book, for example, speaks of his calling as simply "the good manners of the mind"; it is, this scientist says, "the rejection of shadow for substance, of dilemma for solution." The broad point that such men are trying to make (and it is not new) is that science should be looked upon as a way of thinking, a pervasive influence that encompasses the biochemist diligently decoding our genetic molecules and also, say, the musicologist establishing the authenticity of a chorale said to have been composed by Johann Sebastian Bach. Science—the very antithesis of magic—may be at its most demonstrable in the laboratory, where conditions are precise and controlled, but its value is universal, and its universal effect is to prove that the attribute of intelligence is ours, to do with as we will.

Scientists are no longer the novel figures they were twenty years ago, directly after the attack on Hiroshima, but I doubt that the public has yet ceased to think of them as wonder men. For most people, I think, they remain the ones—the special ones—who ended the war with a single ingenious blow. Other monumental ingenuities have since followed, but none cling to the memory like the obliteration that was suddenly visited on Japan. With it, the popular notion of scientists—and of all intellectuals—altered radically, at least in the United States. The conception of them as addled oddballs went by the board. For their tangible feat of clobbering the enemy with finality, a grateful America awarded them the Order of Solid Citizenship, promising never again to doubt that they could meet a payroll. The view persists, I believe, that scientists are the owners of a super Sunday punch, the fellows who can always be counted on to come in and put out the fire. This new image, like the old one, scarcely takes into account the grandeur of the human intellect, its pliancy, its gift for abstraction and synthesization. It is as though we imagined we could emerge from our present morass without recourse to wisdom.

This picture of scientists, of course, is not an

immutable one. It is already being corrected, I suspect, by the spread of scientific education. Further, as the complexity of unsolved problems and the dangers they present grow ever more apparent, increasing numbers of people may develop a fresh reliance on the breadth and usefulness of intellectual processes. I hope this day isn't long in arriving, for the sooner it does, the sooner will the true extent of the scientists' mission become clear: it is, I submit, to teach not only the supreme necessity of the brain but also its inadequacy. The great discovery of the scientific age, I believe, will be ourselves, and it will take all the rational powers of science to show that our salvation lies beyond the rational, at least as we now conceive it. Those powers, I venture to predict, will succeed in solving a wide variety of difficult problems, scientific and social, but new problems will continue to be sighted, like unexpected types of elementary particles. Gradually, it appears to me, we may come to see that final answers are impossible without the play and ascendancy of the human spirit, whose variousness can be comprehended, if at all, only in terms of individuals. We have been caused at long last to face our own primacy, and so be it. Our potential murderers and deliverers are at large, individuals with names and addresses and, very likely, insurance policies. Without intending empty optimism, I think there are signs that we are being overtaken by "an immense self-consciousness," in the phrase of a chemist in this book. One such sign, as far as I am concerned, is the intense scientific curiosity that is currently being concentrated on discovering the secrets of our heredity. Outside the laboratory, there is the steady participation of scientists (and scholars of all sorts) at conferences on international affairs, like the one described in Chapter Five. Such conferences, I have noticed, are rarely attended by men who design weapons, but in recent years, I have also noticed, when interviewing, that the designers now speak of their work with a distinct, even if not an immense, self-consciousness.

In the end, I suppose, the hinge of fate will turn on the ability of people everywhere to do away with suspicion and learn a feeling of trust in each other, which, alas, has more than ever become a form of courage. I would not presume to guess whether this will come to pass before it is too late, but one needn't be a prophet to say that a happy ending is hardly guaranteed. There are scientists, in fact, who assert that even if we conduct ourselves with the utmost intelligence and a full sense of accountability, nature herself will see to our demise. They speak of the phenomenon of life as "a temporary accident," holding that, millennia hence, our planet will be a burnt-out or frozen relic and that life will then be no more existent than it was in the earth's earliest geological ages. Reflecting on this ultimate prospect some years ago, the renowned mathematician Norbert Wiener wrote, "In a very real sense we are shipwrecked passengers on a doomed planet. Yet even in a shipwreck, human decencies and human values do not necessarily vanish, and we must make the most of them. We shall go down, but let it be in a manner to which we may look forward as worthy of our dignity."

Daniel Lang

Menemsha, Massachusetts

1
A Vapor Moving North-Northwest

A few moments after the underground nuclear blast known as Project Gnome went off, at noon on a Sunday, in December, 1961, in a flat and chilly stretch of desert southeast of Carlsbad, New Mexico, all of us who were watching the event from a mound of bulldozed earth four and a half miles due south of ground zero—some four hundred foreign observers, congressmen, government scientists, local citizens, photographers, and reporters—could tell that something had gone wrong. What gave us this impression was not the broad blanket of dust that the explosive—deep below in a formation of salt rock—had jolted out of the desert. Nor was it the bouncing we took—the result of a violent earth tremor that had been caused by the nuclear charge, which was one-fourth as powerful as the Hiroshima bomb. (In the immediate vicinity of the explosion, the desert leaped three feet, and it has yet to descend to its former level.) We had been told to expect these things. Rather, it was the sight of thick and steadily thickening white vapor at the scene of the firing that made us think that plans had miscarried. The vapor was puffing up through an elevator shaft that dropped twelve hundred feet to an eleven-hundred-foot tunnel, at the end of which the explosive, and also much of the project's experimental equipment, had been installed. As we watched the vapor slowly begin to spread, like ground fog, and, rising, vanish into the air, we knew we were witnessing something that we had been practically assured wouldn't happen—venting, or the accidental escape of radioactivity into the atmosphere. "The probability of the experiment venting is so low as to approach the impossible," the Atomic Energy Commission had stated in a comprehensive pamphlet it had published on Project Gnome. Indeed, at a briefing held the previous evening in Carlsbad, where Gnome's headquarters were located, one of the speakers had warned that the shot was just a small one and might well disappoint us as a spectacle. It was the excitement of its underlying idea that made it worthwhile for us to be at the proving ground, we had been told, for Project Gnome marked the opening of the Plowshare Program—a series of nuclear blasts whose purpose, as the name implied, was to turn the atom to peaceful ways. Any number of benefits, we were informed, could flow from these blasts: harbors might be carved out of wasteland in Alaska; oil might be dislodged from shale; abundant sources of water under great mountains might be freed; diamonds might be made out of ordinary carbon.

MODERN CAVEMAN
A scientist (bottom center) surveys the cavity created in less than a second by the underground nuclear experiment called Gnome. (Chap. 1)

below TO PEACE
Khrushchev offers a toast to the signing of the partial test ban treaty. (Wide World wire photo) (Chap. 3)

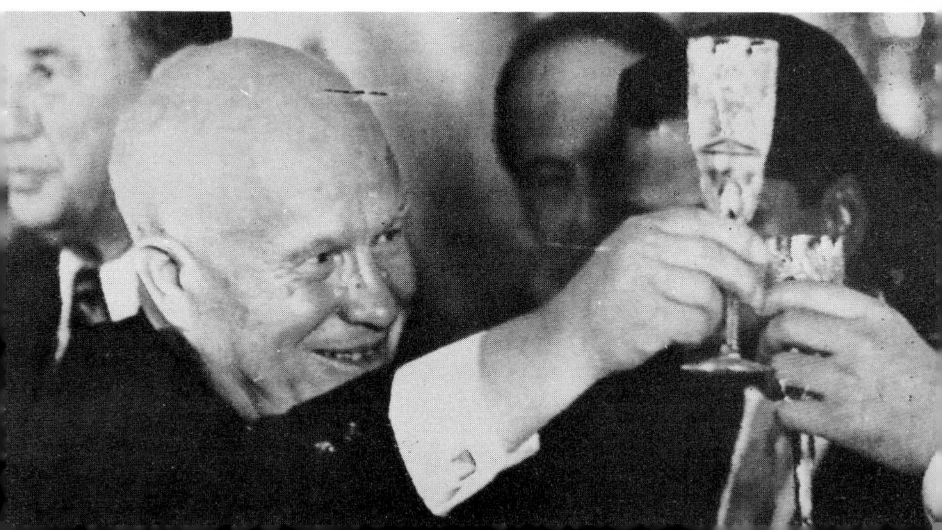

IN A WHITE HOUSE DOORWAY

Presidential Science Adviser Wiesner confers with Mr. Kennedy. (Photo by Jacques Lowe) (Chap. 4)

We were in no danger—the wind was blowing the vapor to the north-northwest of us—but the feeling seemed to take hold that this wasn't necessarily the Prophet Isaiah's day. Before the explosion, a gala mood had prevailed on our barren mound. Local ranchers, their big Stetsons bobbing, had heartily declared that it was a great day for these parts. The operators of nearby potash mines—the world's largest producers of this chemical—had agreed. Their wives, modishly clad, had greeted each other effusively. And Louis M. Whitlock, the manager of the Carlsbad Chamber of Commerce, had assured me, "This bomb is for the good of mankind, and we're for it," as we awaited the explosion. Representative Ben Franklin Jensen, of Iowa, a Republican member of the House Appropriations Committee, had also caught the proper spirit. "There are certain things you just have to spend money on, and Plowshare is one of them," he told me. The foreign visitors lent a certain glamour to the occasion. There was Professor Francis Perrin, for instance—a small, goateed man with elegant manners who was the High Commissioner of France's Commissariat á l'Energie Atomique. The science attaché of the Japanese Embassy was there, too—a young chemist named Dr. Seiichi Ishizaka. Chatting with him shortly before the venting, I had gathered that his government was of two minds about the wisdom of the day's explosion. "Japan is curious," he had told me, smiling politely. The bustle of the many journalists on the scene had added to the festive air. The local people had been fascinated by their activities, clustering around each time Dr. Edward

Teller, the widely celebrated father of the H-bomb, who is also the father of Plowshare, posed for television crews. On the high-school platform in Carlsbad during the previous evening's briefing, he had, in response to a reporter's question, agreed that the Plowshare Program was "too little and too late," and referring to the recent resumption of atmospheric testing in the Soviet Union, had gone on to say, "Plowshare had to wait for permission from the Kremlin, which it is giving in a slightly ungracious manner."

Now, as the insidious gases continued to escape from the shaft, the gala mood faded. An A.E.C. official, speaking over a public-address system from a crudely constructed lectern, announced that all drivers should turn their cars around to facilitate a speedy retreat from the test area. An evacuation, he said, might be in order. A short while later—about half an hour after the detonation—the same official, a calm, affable man by the name of Richard G. Elliott, announced that, according to word from a control point a hundred yards forward, the venting had created a radioactive cloud, low and invisible, which was moving in the general direction of Carlsbad, twenty-three miles away to the northwest. The invisible cloud, which was being tracked by an Air Force helicopter equipped with radiation counters, was expected to miss the town, but it would pass over a section of the highway on which we had driven from Carlsbad. The state police had consequently been instructed to throw up a roadblock there. Until further notice, the only way to reach Carlsbad would be to head southeast and follow a detour of a hundred and fifty miles. Some spectators left at once to take this roundabout route, figuring that they might as well get the trip over and done with, rather than face an indefinite delay. Some other spectators also departed hurriedly; they suspected the A.E.C. of being excessively cautious, and hoped to use the direct highway to Carlsbad before the police could organize their blockade. As things turned out, a few of these motorists did elude the police, only to be intercepted eventually in Carlsbad itself. Seven cars were found to be contaminated; the A.E.C. paid to have them washed down. Two of the passengers, according to the A.E.C., showed slight, easily removable traces of radioactivity, one on his hand and the other on his clothing and hair. As for the cloud, the helicopter that had started tracking it had been forced to return to base when the craft's instruments showed that it was being contaminated. Another machine took its place, and the pilot of this kept the cloud under surveillance until darkness forced him to give up his mission; the cloud was then five miles north of a small town called Artesia, about sixty miles north-northwest of the test site; it had hovered briefly over the eastern edge of the town, and continued in its north-northwesterly path. At the time he took his leave of the cloud, the pilot reported, its radiation was diminishing steadily—a process attributable to nature, rather than to Gnome's artificers.

Fortunately, the countryside over which this gaseous debris was being wafted was only sparsely populated. In fact, this was one of the reasons the explosive had been set off in this particular area. In spite of the reassurances about venting in the pamphlet, the A.E.C. and its chief contractor for Plowshare—the University of California's Lawrence Radiation Laboratory, in Livermore, California—had had this eventuality very much in mind when they planned Gnome. Many precautions had been taken. The tunnel was packed with bags of salt and blocks of concrete, designed to arrest the spread of radioactivity. Wind patterns had been analyzed by the United States Weather Bureau during the entire week before the shot. The day's detonation had, in fact, been delayed four hours until the winds were considered to be blowing in a safe direction. Ranchers for five miles around had been evacuated, tactfully, by being asked to join the Gnome spectators; their cattle, less privileged, had simply been driven off to roam different pastures for the day—or for however long it might take the United States Public Health Service to certify the cleanliness of their familiar acres. The Federal Aviation Agency had been asked to order planes in the area to maintain a certain altitude until further notice. The dryness of the salt formation notwithstanding, the United States Geological Survey had made ground-water surveys of the surrounding area for six months before the shot and would continue to do so for at least a year afterward, in order to keep tabs on any underground movement of radioactive material. Seismic effects had also been anticipated. A special bill had been put through Congress to assure the potash industry of suitable indemnification in the event of damage. On the day of the detonation, no potash miners were on hand to chip at the rose-colored walls of their rough corridors.

Nor were tourists permitted to explore the Carlsbad Caverns, thirty-four miles to the east of the detonation site. Acting on behalf of Project Gnome, the Coast and Geodetic Survey had placed a seismograph inside the Caverns. A member of the Caverns' staff—a naturalist from the National Park Service—was on hand to measure seismic effects in his own way; he watched to see if the blast would ripple one of the still, subterranean ponds that had been created over millennia, partly by drops of water from the cave's stalactites. (It didn't.) In retrospect, perhaps the most significant of all the precautions taken was the relatively last-minute reduction of the yield of the explosive from ten kilotons, as originally planned, to five kilotons. "Whoever made *that* decision, I'd like to shake his hand," an A.E.C. official told me the day after the shot.

Those of us who, like me, were waiting for the roadblock to be lifted, passed the time as best we could. We discussed our reactions to the blast for a while, but, oddly, this soon began to pall. Some of us wandered over to a chuck wagon that the A.E.C. had thoughtfully laid on, and bought ourselves coffee and sandwiches. Now and then, we heard new announcements, of varying interest, on the public-address system. One dealt with the far-flung network of seismic recording stations that had been organized by the Department of Defense. A colonel mounted the lectern to tell us that the network appeared to have functioned well. (He didn't know then that Gnome's seismic signal had been recorded in Scandinavia and Japan.) The firing, the colonel added, had taken place "at exactly one four-thousandth of a second after noon." Returning to the lectern, Elliott told us that, according to the instruments, the radiation at the bottom of the shaft now came to a million roentgens an hour, while on the ground at the top of the shaft the count was ten thousand roentgens an hour—twelve and a half times the lethal exposure for a healthy man.

After a while, some of us went and sat in our cars to read or doze or just get out of the cold. Those who didn't could stare at the shaft, from which vapor was still issuing, or, if they preferred, scan the desert, stubbled with tumbleweed and greasewood and cactus. Only the distant sight of a potash refinery relieved the terrain. Bluish-white smoke was pouring from its tall chimney, its furnace having been left unbanked on this day of days. The refinery lay due northwest, near the Carlsbad road, so I knew that the radioactive gases were bound to mingle with the vapors of the tall chimney. Like my fellow-spectators, though, I had no idea when that would come to pass.

❦

The technical objectives of the day's blast, which were almost entirely in the hands of Livermore scientists, were well planned, it had been impressed on all of us in the course of the briefings before the shot. The central purpose was to see what happened when an atomic explosive was set off in a salt formation—what is called phenomenology. The Livermore people hadn't previously had a chance for such a test, their underground efforts thus far having been limited to military shots in the volcanic tuff of the Nevada test site—a substance that doesn't retain heat nearly as well as salt does. And heat was the key to much of what the researchers were seeking to learn. Gnome would enable them to carry out a heat-extraction experiment, for example—the general idea being to investigate the possibility of tapping for productive uses the inferno of superheated steam and other forms of energy that would result from the detonation. This energy, it was hoped, would be contained in a cavity in the salt that the explosive, low though its yield was, would create in about a tenth of a second. The cavity, if it didn't collapse, would be egg-shaped and glowing, and it would be about a hundred and ten feet in diameter; six thousand tons of molten salt were expected to run down its sides and compose a pool thirty-five feet deep. The cavity would also be "mined," by remote control, for radioactive isotopes—unstable atoms that are produced by a nuclear explosion, a fair percentage of which are valuable in scientific research, medical treatment, and industrial processes. (One of them, strontium 90, which is greatly feared in fallout, may some day be used in long-lived batteries to power unmanned weather stations in god-forsaken regions, a Livermore expert told me.)

For pure researchers, it was thought, Gnome's most interesting data might be gained from the large numbers of neutrons—uncharged particles that are part of the atomic nucleus—that would be produced by the blast. In the instant of the explosion, I had been told, Gnome would release as many neutrons as a laboratory apparatus could release in several thousand years. So plentiful would they be, in fact, that only one out of ten million could be studied. Even so, much new light might be shed on such matters as the different velocities of neutrons and the interaction of these particles, which are usually emitted in bursts that last less than a hundred-millionth of a second, an interval of time that is known in scientific shoptalk as "a shake."

❦

But these technical objectives of Project Gnome were only a part of the Plowshare Program, and the Plowshare Program was something more than a scientific enterprise—a fact that had become apparent in the days immediately preceding the desert shot, when Carlsbad had been rife with briefings, interviews, and informative handouts. The case for Plowshare, in the opinion of some of the foreign observers and other people I talked with, seemed to rest on a variety of grounds. I learned, for example, that the proposed series of blasts had been approved by the A.E.C. four years before, which raised the question of why they were being started at this particular time. Plowshare officials readily acknowledged that the complete answer certainly included the state of international affairs. Was Plowshare, then, a solid program or a passing, virtuous response to the Russian resumption of atmospheric testing? Perhaps Plowshare's name was partly to blame for this questioning attitude. "It sounds a little too much like magic," a foreign scientist remarked. "So many swords are being made just now."

In any event, a day or two before the shot, I discussed Plowshare in Carlsbad with two of its overseers, both of whom were strongly in favor of the program, as one would expect, but in a fairly thoughtful, unmagical way. One of them was John S. Kelly, a bespectacled, mild-mannered man of thirty-nine who directed the A.E.C.'s Division of Peaceful Nuclear Explosives. He saw Plowshare's explosives as scientific and engineering tools. It excited him, he said, to contemplate the excavation jobs that might be performed in the future, like blasting lakes out of the wilderness and breaking up ore deposits that could be leached out. Plowshare represented a continuation of the whole history of explosives, Kelly said. Certainly explosives could be harmful, he conceded, but on the other hand gunpowder had done away with the feudal system and TNT had made possible the mining of fossil fuels.

"But can we afford to guess wrong with nuclear explosives?" I asked. "Don't they represent an ultimate kind of energy?"

"Why not use them for our ultimate good?" Kelly replied.

For an undertaking concerned with the peaceful uses of the atom, I remarked, Plowshare appeared to have its ambiguities. The fissionable material and the equipment for the Gnome explosive, I mentioned, had been taken from our armaments stockpile; the explosive was being concealed from the public gaze, the same as a weapon is; men in uniform had come to Carlsbad for the shot, and were participating actively in its preparation; and among those prominently involved were people from Livermore, which was noted primarily as a center of weapons design.

Kelly was quick to grant that the line between the peaceful and the military sides of the atom was fuzzy. It would be nice, he said, if the two functions could be neatly demarcated, for in that case the Plowshare Program, living up to its name more fully, could have postponed the blasts until war was an obsolete institution. But that wasn't the way things were, in Kelly's view. "We may have to take our peaceful uses when we can," he said.

The other official I talked with was Dr. Gary H. Higgins, the director of the Plowshare Division of the Lawrence Radiation Laboratory. Higgins was a soft-spoken chemist of thirty-four, whose desk in his Carlsbad office was adorned, when I saw it, with a small ceramic gnome he had bought in a department store. Like Kelly, he believed that nuclear explosives had a great peacetime future. "Within five to fifteen years, they'll be basic to our industrial economy," he told me. "They'll help us get at raw materials we need for our growing population. It may take us time to make use of them. After all, forest husbandry developed only when the nation was practically deforested." He was delighted that the United States was moving ahead with Plowshare, but not, he told me, because it relieved him of his weapons duties at Livermore. The two kinds of work, he felt, were not pure opposites; there was a difference between weapons and war, he said, just as there was between a police force and murder. But whether an idea like Plowshare or an arms race was to dominate our lives in the years ahead was another matter. It depended, Higgins thought, on whether mankind could eventually achieve an immense self-consciousness. "It would not cater to the oversimplified images that religion and ethics tend to give us," Higgins said. "It would enable us to recognize our weaknesses. We'd know our motives for acting the way we do, and what else is it that counts but intent, whether shots are called Plowshare or something else?"

❦

It was almost four hours after the detonation when I left the bulldozed mound in the desert. The roadblock hadn't yet been lifted, but to a number of us that didn't matter. We were chafing to get away, although not for any sensible reason I heard expressed. Perhaps the others felt, as I did, a sense of rebellion and indignation at being trapped by a mysterious, invisible antagonist. In the distance, the refinery's tall chimney continued to surrender its thick plume of smoke, giving no sign, of course, whether there had yet been any mingling with the radioactive cloud. Absurdly, I felt like going to the refinery to find out. Around us, shadows were beginning to fall on the desert, making it seem more limitless than ever, and underscoring our marooned condition.

At any rate, when a rancher who was among the spectators mentioned to some of us that certain back roads might bring one out on the Carlsbad highway three or four miles beyond the police blockade, I was off at once, in a car with two other men—Ken Fujisaki, a young correspondent for a Tokyo newspaper, the *Sankei Shimbun,* and David Perlman, a reporter for the San Francisco *Chronicle*. The rancher, who himself was in no hurry to leave, had said he hadn't used those particular back roads in fifteen years, but at the time this remark had struck us as irrelevant. Our immediate goals were a windmill and a gas well—two landmarks that, the rancher had said, might soon guide us on our way to Carlsbad.

"How would you like to spend two weeks in a fallout shelter?" Perlman, who was driving, asked me as he impatiently started the car.

After a ten-minute drive over a bumpy, rutted road, we were at the gas well. We were also at a dead end. As we were looking at each other in puzzlement, we heard the honk of a car horn behind us, and discovered that we had been leaders of men. Nine other cars had followed us to the dead end; we had been too intent on our flight from safety to notice them. One of the vehicles was a small orange government truck, and another was a sports car—a dirty, white Triumph whose driver wore goggles. Some of us got out of our cars, conferred ignorantly, and decided to go back and follow a dirt road that had intersected the one we were on. This road also came to a dead end. Backtracking, we tried another, and then another. The fourth ran parallel to a ranch fence, on the other side of which were cattle and horses. Beyond the field they were in we could see the Carlsbad highway, only a couple of miles off. The fence seemed to run on endlessly, leading nowhere. Our caravan halted, and a few of us climbed a stile to seek advice at the ranch. We found a young Mexican hand, who obligingly corralled the animals, and opened a gate into a muddy, reddish road that crossed the field. In no time we were on the highway to

Carlsbad. To get there, we had gone east, north, west, and northeast. Now we passed the potash refinery, its tall stack still smoking. I looked at it as long as I could. No police intercepted us. When we reached the Project Gnome office in Carlsbad, we learned that the roadblock had been called off fifteen minutes after our departure. Perlman asked that he be gone over with a radiation counter. He proved to be fine, which meant the rest of us were.

When I arrived at my motel, the manager phoned me. He was a transplanted Englishman with whom I had made friends. Since I was leaving the next day, I thought perhaps he was calling to say goodbye, but it was Project Gnome that was on his mind.

"I'm sick in bed, you see, so *I'm* quite all right, but it's the staff—" he began. A guest, he said, had told the cashier in the restaurant not to touch the money of anyone who had been to the test. The cashier had become hysterical. Then a policeman had come and collected two other members of the staff to have them "counted" at the Gnome office; the two had been spectators at the shot and had been among those who eluded the roadblock.

"There's no need for any concern, is there?" the manager asked me uneasily. "I mean, those men out there know what they're doing, don't they?"

I could hear him breathing at the other end of the phone, waiting for my answer.

"Of course they do," I said. "Of course everything's all right."

2
A Mustering of the Troops

Diplomats aren't alone in seeking disarmament. The public, too, sometimes takes a hand in this delicate, momentous endeavor, the best-known occasion being Britain's Aldermaston March, which was held for a number of years over the Easter weekend, when thousands of marchers, in a kind of pilgrimage, walked all or part of a fifty-mile route between the Berkshire town of Aldermaston and London in order to protest the possibility of nuclear war. When the March first took place, in 1958, Aldermaston was chosen as one end of the route because it was the site of Great Britain's Atomic Weapons Research Establishment. As a popular demonstration, the Aldermaston March, which I witnessed in the spring of 1963, was unburdened by cares of state. Its deliberations were not hidden by carved, imposing portals, such as one finds at the Palais des Nations, in Geneva, where diplomats have for years been attempting to reach disarmament agreements. The March's conference chamber was the open road, and its language, unconcerned with treaty clauses, was the simple hortatory one of slogans. The March, in short, represented the pure opposite of the diplomatic approach; it was a chance for ordinary citizens to voice their impatience with and distrust of international power moves. "We want to counter the uncertainties of clever, sophisticated politics with a moral quality," I was told in London the week before Easter by Hugh Brock, editor of the pacifist newspaper *Peace News* and a leader of the Campaign for Nuclear Disarmament, the organization that sponsors the March. "I'm not saying that politicians are evil, but the machinery of government does include military methods, and we're hoping to keep the finger off the button through popular protest." It was my curiosity about popular protest that drew me to England, for in its several years of existence the C.N.D., for better or worse, had come to symbolize the public outcry throughout the world over the undiminished arms race. The Aldermaston March, I knew, had been copied in over thirty countries, and the procession I watched included Americans, Germans, Irish, Pakistanis, Iraqis, French, Cypriotes, Indians, Kurds, Ghanaians, Swedes, South Africans, and Japanese, one of the last being a Buddhist priest who had travelled to Aldermaston from Hiroshima. Hundreds of C.N.D. members had been arrested since 1958 for staging sitdowns in front of important government buildings in London and at rocket bases, and for trying to block the runways of military airfields. "I don't believe that any of us have ever been arrested for assault," I was informed at Aldermaston shortly before the March began by Peter Moule, a bearded young man who was national secretary of the Committee of 100, one of the many groups that made up the C.N.D., but one that, unlike most of the others, believed in civil disobedience. "Sometimes a novice will resist the police in some way, but the rest of us, as we're being carried off to the van, will encourage him to stop struggling and go limp. That's the technique we use when the police pick us up. It dramatizes our belief in non-violence. One time when I was being arrested, I remember, one of the bobbies carrying me offered to pay my fine."

I was in Aldermaston at noon on Good Friday for the start of the four-day March. In a large, open field, thousands of people were assembling, many of them hoisting banners and placards bearing slogans that denounced nuclear war, fallout from bomb tests, and enormous outlays for armaments. ("Calories Not Catastrophes!" and "Activity with Us Today or Radioactivity Tomorrow!" were two that I recall.) The crowd seemed predominantly youthful, although, I was told, the age distribution would broaden somewhat as the distance to London shortened. "Young people are far more aware of the implications of science than their elders are," I was told by Ritchie Calder, a professor of international relations at the University of Edinburgh and the vice-chairman of the C.N.D.'s Executive Committee. "This march expresses their sense of frustration about current politics." A few of the marchers were taking pictures of each other, and from here and there in the meadow arose the strains of guitars and folk singing; a jazz combo warmed up furiously for a few minutes, apparently itching to get the show on the road. Over a public-address system, instructions to march in an orderly fashion and stay four abreast were being blared forth. A trickle of demonstrators shuttled to and from a nearby pub, some returning with glasses in hand.

A restless, uncertain air hung over the field, and as I watched, I reflected on the purposes of the March, at least as these had been explained to me by C.N.D. leaders in London. The underlying aim, I had been told, was to upset the current pattern of disarmament negotiations, which had so far produced nothing but a dangerous international stalemate. This hardening pattern, the C.N.D. felt, called for solvents in the form of "new elements" and "graduated initiatives," and these, in effect, came down to unilateral British atomic disarmament. If Britain withdrew from the so-called Nuclear Club, it was argued, the step might break up the impasse, and create momentum for disarmament everywhere. Certainly Britain itself stood to gain by quitting the misbegotten club, the theory went, since it could scarcely afford the extravagant dues, and this money could be freed for such badly needed public facilities as schools and hospitals. When I inquired about the presence of the Kurds, Pakistanis, Iraqis, and others whose governments had nothing to be unilateral about, I was told that they were on hand primarily to publicize the worldwide interest in disarmament.

My talks in London, however, had left me with

questions. For one thing, there appeared to be little interest in Britain's getting rid of conventional, or non-nuclear, weapons, which left an ambiguity as to the C.N.D.'s attitude toward disarmament in general. Far more important, to my way of thinking, was the absence of any plan for bringing about the resignation of other members of the Nuclear Club. There was some hopeful mention of this in the C.N.D.'s literature, to be sure, but that was all. I looked in vain for details of ways to persuade other countries to adopt similar unilateral positions. And there was certainly nothing about any timetable for their doing so. Indeed, I encountered an almost diplomatic evasiveness on the part of C.N.D. leaders when I tried to discuss the implications of having the United States go unilateral before the Soviet Union did. This vagueness, as far as I could see, left open the main question with which the nuclear powers had been grappling at thousands of conference sessions, in Geneva and elsewhere: namely, how to go about giving up weapons without inviting attack. I had been told by Vanessa Redgrave, the actress, who is an outspoken and active unilateralist, "I would not presume to suggest what other nations should do. It is difficult enough to communicate with one's own countrymen."

The plain fact was, as leading members of the C.N.D. admitted to me rather freely, the March and all the theorizing back of it amounted to a protest against a sort of world in which it was possible to look up every day and see planes that carry H-bombs flying about, to know that submarines were wandering underseas with similar cargoes, and to breathe irradiated particles from the Pacific, the Sahara, and Siberia. It was a protest so sweeping that it could be made on behalf of anyone, whether prime minister or porter, and this abstract quality, I gathered, sometimes left even its most ardent advocates with the feeling that they were tilting at windmills. One of them, a man who had spent months in prison for acts of civil disobedience, admitted to me that he felt a certain envy of Gandhi, whose doctrine of non-violence was an article of faith for many of the marchers. "Gandhi's objectives were limited, compared to ours," he said. "He was able to meet issues squarely. When he led his followers against British rule, he knew exactly who his adversary was. So does Martin Luther King today. We, too, resort to direct action, but we do so with divided minds. Some of us believe we should concentrate on the bomb alone, but others ask, 'Isn't the bomb merely one manifestation of a sick society, and aren't our activities too narrowly conceived?' "

❦

When the March finally got under way, in the early afternoon, under a pale, chilly sky, I watched much of it go by from a slightly elevated spot two or three hundred yards down the road from the assembly grounds. Standing with me were a few other spectators, including a reporter friend and an elderly lady who wore, for the gala day, several buttons bearing the drooping-cross symbol of the C.N.D. Behind us was a barbed-wire fence surrounding a group of ordinary-looking, low brick buildings—the Atomic Weapons Research Establishment. There were numbers of police about, seeing to it that the road, a narrow country one, was kept open to traffic. At the head of the parade was a gray van, the C.N.D.'s mobile headquarters, in the back of which I saw a cheerful-looking gray-haired woman, Mrs. Peggy Duff, secretary of the C.N.D.'s Executive Committee, whom I had met in London, and who had charge of the weekend's logistics. Not far behind the van, and keeping to one side of the road, slowly marched the three leaders of the procession, all of them people in their middle years, and all of them veterans of every March that had so far taken place: Professor Calder, whose children, I had been told, were also marching, somewhere behind him; Canon Lewis John Collins, of St. Paul's Cathedral, chairman of the C.N.D. and a man active in many worthy causes, who was wearing his cassock; and Jacquetta Hawkes, the wife of J. B. Priestley, a handsome woman in a broad-brimmed maroon hat, who marched with a long, determined stride, her eyes shining as though fixed on some distant vision of glory. Among the marchers close behind these three was a smiling young man, his limbs useless, who was being pushed in a wheelchair, and several rows behind him there came a solid phalanx of standard-bearers, holding aloft scores of tall black banners on which rallying cries were printed in white. It was only after these massed flags had passed that I realized the length of the procession. It extended perhaps a mile—a long, wavy column that would have depressed a drill sergeant.

The composition of the parade, I now saw, was far more varied than it had seemed amidst the scattered activity in the open field. More older people were present than I had realized, many of them fit-looking, pink-cheeked men and women in tweeds and stout boots, who advanced jauntily and gave the impression of having discovered the joys of a fifty-mile hike. Whole families had turned out; in a dozen instances that I bothered to count, parents were guiding baby carriages over the uneven Berkshire road. So many different beliefs and points of view were represented by banners and posters announcing the affiliations of various groups of marchers that it was hard to see how all of these people could be drawn together for even a weekend. "Baptists on the March," proclaimed one banner. "The Bomb Does Not Suit Our Book," said another, borne by marchers with other banners that identified them as Christian Pacifists. Quakers, earnest and silent, were ranged behind "To Resist War Is to Uphold Human Dignity." The Buddhist priest came along, slowly and steadily beating a tambour, his movements unimpeded by his flowing orange robe. Episcopalians, Methodists, and Catholics were there, and so was a man who had thrust anti-Catholic literature on me back at the assembly grounds, identifying himself as a member of the National Secular Society. Communists, Conservatives, Labourites, and Liberals passed with their banners. The London Federation of Anarchists made its appearance, and the elderly C.N.D. woman next to me greeted them with a genial call of "Bomb throwers!" Perhaps the most ingratiating watchword I saw was "Woodcraft Folk Span the World with Friendship." An Esperanto group shuffled past, and so did one made up of theatrical people, and there were vast numbers of college students and dons. *"Pax Potior Bello"* was the learned motto of London University's Birkbeck College, and that of one of the Cambridge groups was "1945: Hiroshima; 19??: Cambridge in Ruins." It was the youth of the collegians and younger participants that gave the parade what cohesion it had, linking the disparate affiliations. Youth was wildly on display. It was from the young people that the parade drew its music, scores of youthful guitarists among them strumming away, providing accompaniment for boys and girls who sang heartily of strontium 90 and button pushers and Polaris missiles. There were even guitarists in reserve, since a number of marchers who weren't strumming had guitar cases strapped to their backs. For that matter, most of the marchers had something strapped to their backs—sleeping bags, bedrolls, knapsacks. Their dress was generally rough and practical, and in a great many instances also determinedly nonconformist; uniforms of blue jeans, zippered black windbreakers, and long, sharp-pointed shoes were to be seen everywhere. One teen-ager, marching behind a placard that read "We Don't Dig Doom," was wearing what may have been a hand-me-down from his father—an R.A.F. pilot's jacket, its brown leather scuffed and its fur collar moth-eaten. What little headgear there was consisted of battered fedoras and dusty derbies; nearly all these were sported by larkish members of occasional jazz combos. There was an immense quantity of hair to be seen, hundreds of male marchers looking as though barbers were their worst enemies. The beardless ones couldn't easily be told apart from their lipstickless girl friends. Numerous couples marched past with arms linked and knapsacks bouncing in unison. One couple embraced as they came into view, and the elderly C.N.D. lady next to me nodded approvingly. "It does people good, doesn't it, to see that nuclear disarmers aren't crabby old saints?" she said.

Together with my reporter friend, who had a car, I left my vantage point to find Mrs. Duff and ask her how things were going. We caught up with her where the van had halted, in a roadside clearing that was just beginning to be invaded for a tea break. During our chat, I asked Mrs. Duff, a practical, bustling woman without any Messianic airs, if she thought C.N.D. members were more concerned than other people with staying alive.

Mrs. Duff smiled. "Oh, no, not at all," she replied. "But people do tend to avoid facing up to the possibility of nuclear war. Besides, they don't believe there's anything they can do about the situation. Whatever you may think about the C.N.D., we're not guilty of *that.*"

I asked what she thought of international negotiations as an approach to disarmament.

"The more effective they are, the better," Mrs. Duff said. "I'm not convinced, however, that it's best to rely on only one approach. Disarmament may be too complex for that. We want to create a climate of public opinion that will make it possible for political leaders to feel that they can realistically act in behalf of disarmament."

I mentioned the intellectuals who were active in the C.N.D.—philosophers, scientists, writers. Did she think, I asked, that they might be more usefully engaged in pondering disarmament ideas than in mere marching and sit-downs?

Mrs. Duff wasn't at all sure that thinking and marching excluded each other—and, in any event, she observed, no one joined the C.N.D. for purely cerebral reasons, least of all the kind of people I was talking about. "Intellectuals like to contribute unintellectually," she said. "That's their way of making a moral gesture."

❦

The marchers' destination that first day was the city of Reading, about ten miles northeast of Aldermaston, and my reporter friend dropped me there on his way back to London. At Reading, the marchers would be bedding down in twelve big rented tents, the largest of which, I was told, had done service with a circus; two thousand marchers would sleep under it on the ground, whose dampness would be slightly offset by strips of polyethylene. I had a leisurely meal in an empty restaurant, my sole company being Mrs. Duff's thought that diplomacy alone might not be able to bring about disarmament. It reminded me that diplomats, for their part, had their feelings about popular pressure. In the summer of 1960, when I had been in Geneva, an American negotiator had paid it a sort of occupational compliment. "I find public agitation good for my morale," he had told me. "I work better when I know that everyone's interested in what I'm doing." Just before going to Aldermaston, however, I had encountered a different diplomatic attitude. The diplomat in this instance was the Joint Parliamentary Under-Secretary of State for Foreign Affairs, whom I had called on in Downing Street, and he had told me that he thought disarmament discussions should be confined to the negotiating table. "If we thought that marching through the streets contributed to a disarmament arrangement, we would shake the hand of everybody in the C.N.D.," the diplomat told me. "But that organization is the relic of a cranky fringe that started in the seventeenth century, when extreme Puritanism got out of hand. It's made up of people who can't see beyond one fixed idea, like certain constituents of mine who keep writing me about cruelty to tortoises."

I wandered about Reading awhile after leaving the restaurant, and then started up London Street, which I knew was on the marchers' route. It was not an elegant thoroughfare, but it had a quiet, inviting broadness; its shops were closed for the Easter weekend, and a few residents, poorly dressed, were idling on stoops or looking out of the windows of parallel rows of drab three-story houses. I hadn't gone very far when, at the crest of a mild slope, I saw the marchers coming in my direction. I stood still on the sidewalk, awaiting the procession, aware that people around me were deserting their stoops for the curb and that windows were being flung open. The pace of the procession seemed weary, but as the marchers drew nearer, I could see that their faces were cheerful enough; perhaps their dispositions were buoyed by the knowledge that their day was nearly over. I watched a part of the procession file past, and then, curious to see how it felt to march, I stepped down from the curb and joined one of the contingents—a C.N.D. group from Kent, as it happened—whose members received me as though I had signed on with them back home. Almost as soon as I began to move down London Street, I felt an absurd superiority toward the slackers in the windows and on the sidewalks, and then a sense of exhilaration at being one of thousands, so many of them so young. The music sounded stirring now that I was marching to it and encircled by it, and one of the songs brought me back to the reminiscent mood I had been in at lunch. Its words returned to me the instant the guitarists and singers started up. I could have joined in singing it, but I didn't. The song was "I Ain't Gonna Study War No More," and I had sung it about twenty-five years earlier, as an undergraduate at an anti-Fascist demonstration. Since those days, I had witnessed two atomic explosions, and the song, it seemed to me, was up against even more now than it had been then.

I slipped out of the ranks after half an hour or so, by which time the March had turned into another street, and was approaching King's Meadows, where the tents were set up. I was no sooner back on the sidewalk than a pair of young men who not only were clean-shaven but had on neckties approached me and began to extoll the C.N.D. They were members of the organization's "flying column," and their assignment was to tell onlookers about the purpose of the March. The two were biochemistry students at Liverpool University.

"People aren't against the C.N.D., but they're not for it, either," one of them said. "They're not for anything, except apathy."

"That's why the March is such a morale boost for us," the other said. "It's a relief to know that there are other people who think as you do. It keeps you going the rest of the year."

The parade began to disperse short of King's Meadows, the marchers drifting singly or in small groups in the general direction of the encampment. I came upon Canon Collins walking alone; he had put on a blue beret and was puffing a pipe. He spoke of the March with satisfaction. "It's not a religious occasion, but it's on the moral side, on the right road," he said. "In a sense, it's one of the best ways for a Christian to spend Easter weekend. I regard the March as a showing of the flag, if you will, a mustering of the troops."

King's Meadows was a mob scene. The marchers were all over the place, looking for friends and for sleeping places in the fading light. Some were making for a sandwich counter, and others were trailing off to a first-aid station, where C.N.D. doctors and nurses were ministering to the day's casualties, most of them blister cases. There was even a news vender on hand, as I discovered when a young beatnik came up to me and said rather diffidently, *"Freedom, Freedom"*—which was the name of an anarchist journal he was selling. Mrs. Duff, harried but poised, was meeting a series of emergencies; there was a chance, she informed me in a desperate aside, that the tents might not be able to hold everybody. I was surprised. The whole human race, it appeared to me, had already entered the largest one. But more marchers, as I could now see for myself, were continuing to enclose themselves within its billowing canvas—men and women, colored and white, lame and strapping, thin and fat, infants and young parents. When the circus tent was finally filled, all of them, strangers and friends alike, would share the night on its grassy floor, their bond presumably a desire to live.

❦

By Saturday night, the March reached the town of Slough, twenty miles from London, and on Easter Sunday morning its phalanx of standard-bearers took up positions outside the walled gray massiveness of Windsor Castle, a few miles away, where the Queen was spending the holiday. The weather had been raw and the blister cases had increased, but the C.N.D. members, milling in the streets until the March resumed, were more lively than ever. Their manner was cocky, and in fact had turned almost taunting. The reason for this could be found on the front page of every London paper. The day before, while the marchers plodded from Reading to Slough, several hundred direct-actionists had broken away along the route and tried to storm a theretofore secret underground bunker. Their act had been inspired by leaflets handed out during the bivouac at Reading; these had revealed the bunker to be the site of a regional seat of government in the event of an H-bomb attack on London. Police on duty at "Regional Seat of Government 6," as the bunker was officially known, had, with the aid of reinforcements and dogs, repelled the raiders, and were now out looking for the unknown authors and distributors of the leaflets, which had revealed the positions of a dozen bunkers throughout Britain. The press had seized upon the incident to question the efficiency of the government's security setup, but that, I gathered, didn't impress the C.N.D. members as much of an issue. It was the details of the pamphlet, the sight of the bunker itself, and its defense by the police that had them keyed up. The marchers with whom I talked seemed to feel that they had exposed, for all the world to see, the mentality that could countenance the possibility of a nuclear war. This, it seemed to me, was hardly news, but that point wasn't worth making to most of the marchers that morning, nor did it seem that they were prepared to imagine that, in the absence of an international system of arms control, the idea of designating emergency seats of government was as reasonable as, say, that of having Prince Charles on hand to succeed his mother. They were convinced that their actions had produced tangible evidence to justify their cause, and all morning, in Windsor, one could hear dark, indignant references to anonymous villains—"The bastards!" "The stinking hypocrites!" "The rats!" All morning, too, reporters were kept busy chasing down rumors of fresh exploits of direct action—most of them, according to the rumors, about to be perpetrated under the direction of an extremist member of the Committee of 100, a volatile young man who was a history teacher in a Cambridge secondary school and who happened to be wearing a long black oilskin coat. None of the rumors came to anything, however, and the day proceeded with two orderly events that had been planned by the C.N.D.'s leadership—which, incidentally, officially deplored the attempted overthrow of Regional Seat of Government 6. The first action was to present the Queen with a communication informing her of why the C.N.D. was in town, on the ground that "as the Constitutional Head of our State, you should know our purpose; and that, as a mother, you cannot be unconcerned about peace and the fate of future generations." An Oxford housewife assigned to deliver the letter at the castle was unable to say, when she emerged, who had accepted it on behalf of the Queen. The day's second planned event took place in the long meadow of Runnymede, on the banks of the Thames, where the marchers signed a "Magna Carta, 1963." "At Runnymede, in June 1215, King John was compelled to grant the Magna Carta," this document began. "Wilful tyranny had to concede the rights of the individual.... Seven hundred and fifty years later that liberty is threatened by a greater tyranny—the Tyranny of the Bomb." It concluded with a demand for "freedom from fear, from the nightmare of senseless statesmanship which relies on the balance of terror; the right of... children to live, uncrippled by nuclear poisons; the right of every individual to say: 'I shall not be a party to nuclear murder.'"

❦

The March had its biggest turnout in London. Thousands of metropolitan sympathizers, rising in their flats early on Easter Monday, took the Underground to Acton Green, on the outskirts of the capital, to join those who had walked all the way from Aldermaston. Perhaps the continuing headlines over the bunker incident had something to do with the size of the crowd. In any event, when, late in the afternoon, the marchers trooped into Hyde Park for a rally that was to end the weekend's festivities, their column was fully two miles long. But London, too, was long, and the great city took the March in stride. The red double-decker buses lumbered alongside the parade, pausing now and then for queues of passengers, who had to tread their way through the marchers' ranks; venders of *Sanity,* the C.N.D.'s newspaper, who were out in force for the day, were mistaken for venders of less intense newspapers; in Kensington, two matronly women whom I happened to notice didn't turn to look at the March until they had finished admiring the violets and irises in a florist's window. How could Londoners be sure that the C.N.D. wasn't taking itself too seriously? Other demonstrations had wound through the streets in the past, and they, too, had claimed that the fate of the world hung on their cause. Indeed, Miss Redgrave recalled one such past cause from the speakers' platform in Hyde Park when, reading exquisitely from the memoirs of Mrs. Emmeline Pankhurst, she found lessons for the nuclear disarmers in the struggles of the woman's-suffrage movement.

The day seemed to keep the marchers at a high pitch. During a lunch break before the rally, a member of the League of Empire Loyalists, shouting "Traitor!," tossed a sack of flour at Canon Collins, whitening his cassock. As the marchers passed through Whitehall en route to Hyde Park, they were heartened by the sight of a middle-aged woman who, ignoring the traffic that whizzed past her, was staging a sitdown on a cushion in the gutter before Admiralty House, where the Prime Minister was in residence while 10 Downing Street was being renovated. At Hyde Park, the actor Peter O'Toole put in a personal appearance and, like Miss Redgrave, drew a hand from the marchers, who were gathered on the grass in a swarming throng. The Buddhist priest from Japan was introduced from the platform, and was also roundly cheered; a superb folk-singing team entertained; and the novelist Alan Sillitoe contributed a poem called "The Rats."

On the way to Hyde Park, I had hopped aboard the C.N.D.'s slow-moving gray van. Mrs. Duff was in it. She was alone, except for the driver, and we talked awhile, facing each other on benches that ran along the sides. Through the rear opening, we could see the procession's awkward, crooked ranks, its placards with crudely lettered slogans bobbing unevenly. It would take a fortune-teller, Mrs. Duff said, to know what lay ahead for the C.N.D., since events had so much to do with its ups and downs. Such events as the Cuban crisis and the bogging down of disarmament negotiations might underscore the organization's usefulness, but then others would come along and obscure it. For example, she said, the bombers that wheeled overhead each day bearing thermonuclear devices were about to be withdrawn as obsolete. Very likely, too, the American bases in Britain would presently be vacated, now that Polaris-missile submarines were patrolling the seas. And next year there quite possibly wouldn't even be an Atomic Weapons Research Establishment at Aldermaston from which to start the March; the government had announced that it might very well declare the plant redundant. The March could start from somewhere else, of course, Mrs. Duff said, but there were other complications. Many members of the C.N.D., she explained, had a feeling that the March was played out—that it was becoming too institutionalized to arouse fresh public interest in disarmament, which was the C.N.D.'s reason for being. The organization, pulled this way and that as it now was, wasn't likely to get far in the field of practical politics, as some of its members dreamed that it might, nor was civil disobedience likely to attract widespread support, as other members believed, so long as its practitoners' aims remained hazy and debatable.

"We've reached a time for rethinking," Mrs. Duff said as we watched Canon Collins and Professor Calder marching along behind us, smiling about something or other. Whatever new thoughts might be forthcoming, the organization would probably never be entirely rid of a certain vagueness. All it could really do, she went on, was stand up and say no to the threat of war, over and over, in as many ways as it knew how. That was no small mission, Mrs. Duff said, and vagueness wasn't necessarily weakness. "We can count our victories," she asserted as the van slowed down for a light. "The most important one, I should say, is that we've made millions of people, here and throughout the world, aware of the meaning of a nuclear war. It's going to be a job keeping them that way."

3
Visits to a Conference

Like the Aldermaston marchers, diplomats of duly constituted governments shared a desire to save the world from extermination, but their methods of achieving this end were distinctly undemonstrative. I observed this during three visits I made to Geneva, about a year apart, to follow the progress of the test-ban conference that began there in 1958 for a seemingly endless run. Delegates of the United States, Russia, and Great Britain—the first three powers to possess nuclear weapons—were convening in one of the ornate rooms of the marbled, labyrinthine Palais des Nations in an effort to work out a treaty that they hoped would ban the testing of such weapons by present and future members of the Nuclear Club. (The delegates' sessions were formally known as the Conference on the Discontinuance of Nuclear Weapons Tests.) From each trip to the international capital on the Rhône, I brought back various observations concerning the progress of the deliberations. The following excerpts show how the mood of the conference, which eventually culminated in a partial test-ban treaty, fluctuated between one of high hope and one of downright bleakness—which was probably to be expected, since the delegates, and their superiors back home, were contending with issues that were always complex and sometimes unprecedented.

August, 1960

On the face of it, the conference's projected treaty is singularly undemanding. If it should ever become effective, it would not deprive the three conferees of their existing stockpiles of atomic and hydrogen bombs. It would not even keep them from augmenting those stockpiles with newly manufactured weapons. Its sole injunction would be against the testing—the exploding—of such weapons. Essentially, then, the conference is concerned with the solution of a health problem. Yet the widespread fear of fall-out and its dire effects does not appear to preoccupy the diplomats here, though they are perfectly willing to concede that this universal anxiety is the true reason for their presence in Geneva. In the main, their thinking, as far as I have been able to gather from talking with them, is geared to the traditional considerations of power politics—considerations that in this instance are complicated by differing ideological tenets. Whatever progress the conference has achieved, therefore, is traceable to the familiar principle of national interest. And since the progress has been substantial (more than half the treaty has been initialled), the working out of a treaty—the right kind, that is—apparently continues to serve the national interests of all three of the powers involved. The representatives of these powers are well aware, as off-the-record talks make clear, that a test-ban treaty accepted the world over would have the effect of keeping the Nuclear Club exclusive, since by preventing any aspirant for membership from testing whatever weapons he had developed it would prevent him from finding out whether he was squandering his treasury on stockpiles of duds.

The Russians, it appears, would dearly love to see a treaty in operation before their Chinese comrades can acquire a nuclear arsenal, while the Americans feel that a bombless West Germany is likely to remain pliable to American foreign policy. "Supposing Egypt and Israel start making atomic bombs?" an Englishman asked me rhetorically. Moreover, the members of the three delegations realize that if their conference drags on long enough, the Nuclear Club may undergo a wholesale expansion—an unthinkable prospect, since it would make a mockery of power itself. A Guatemala, for example, armed with nuclear weapons (and the means of their delivery) would, for all practical purposes, be the military peer of any of the formidable powers of today.

Given the incentives of the conference, all of them valid for only a limited period, it may seem surprising that since October 31, 1958, after hundreds of formal sessions at the Palais, scores of informal ones elsewhere, and any number of small parties thrown by this or that plenipotentiary in order to soothe the frayed nerves of his opposite numbers, the conferees should still not have completed a pact. This surprise evaporates, however, when one takes into account the rampant distrust between the Soviet Union and the United States—a distrust that tends to stigmatize any kind of objective approach to the issues at hand as a dangerous failure to keep alert. (The British, while studiously siding with the Americans at the conference table itself, seek in many ways to exert a moderating influence on the two mighty opponents.)

"There is no treaty in the basket yet," I was told by a senior British delegate here, "but it is my judgment that these talks have gone further than any others dealing with weapons toward establishing the principle of control—toward extracting precise assurances that the other chap is living up to his word. All past disarmament talks have broken down over this question of control. Perhaps these test-ban talks are giving us a completely fresh chance at the establishment of this principle." If the principle ever should be established, the diplomat went on, disarmament itself might follow, and, with it, the dissolution of the Nuclear Club. For a moment, I imagined he was about to utter the word "peace," but he was too seasoned a diplomat to do so before an audience of one in his embassy office on a quiet Saturday afternoon. He did, however, permit himself one final speculation. "Control, control," he said. "That could be the beginning of manners among nations."

❦

The secret of the conference's long life (as well as of the threat of sudden death that perennially hangs over it) is, once more, suspicion. Time and again, suspicion has supplied some new snag just when matters were rolling smoothly along. One is told about this suspicion in talks with the delegates at their embassy-villa offices or at sidewalk cafés along the Rhône or at those purposeful cocktail parties where no one ever seems to get drunk. The talks are outspoken, but it is understood that they are not for attribution; only the Soviet ambassador, Semyon K. Tsarapkin, a stocky, vigorous man in his middle fifties with a prognathous jaw, placed no such restriction on an interview I had with him—possibly in the belief that he was not entitled to this amenity of the capitalist press. The distrust that pervades the conference is largely of American and Russian making. (The British distrust the distrust.) Each power fears that the other will cheat by clandestinely testing, and thereby improving, its bombs. The United States believes that the Russians are capable of doing this behind their Iron Curtain. The Soviet Union believes that this country's plans for conducting underground nuclear explosions are not designed to improve methods of detecting such detonations, as is officially claimed, but are, in effect, a pretext for war games.

As far as the writing of the treaty goes, the omnipresent suspicion has steadily asserted itself in the form of a seemingly implacable struggle between what are referred to here as the Adequatists and the Perfectionists. The Perfectionists maintain that any attempt to control nuclear tests is too risky unless the safeguards are scientifically foolproof. The Adequatist position, which is popular with both the British public and the British Foreign Office, favors a treaty whose provisions would "strongly deter" sneak shots by setting up machinery that would provide "a very good chance" of their detection. "We have a choice of evils to make," one British diplomat, a non-scientist of Adequatist views, told me. "On the one hand, we know that tensions and fears may erupt into disaster if unlimited testing of bombs is permitted. On the other hand, we don't want to present the Russians, or any other nation, with loopholes for cheating. I would prefer to be a Perfectionist, but science itself prevents that. It is constantly changing —coming up with new findings, discarding old so-called facts. Its restlessness has convinced me that one cannot make political decisions on the basis of science alone. The way people behave out of their instinct for self-preservation must also be weighed."

Neither the policy of the United States nor that of the Soviet Union is easily categorized. In the case of the Russians, one rumor in this city of rumors has the Kremlin so eager for a treaty (the reasons vary) that it is practically *In*adequatist. Another rumor, however, has Tsarapkin resisting the pressures of military elements back home who not only want a Perfectionist pact, if there is to be a pact at all, but want it in a hurry, because they suspect that their American counterparts have secretly resumed testing. One does not need to be alert for rumors to learn the American position, since our officials are far more approachable than the Soviet Union's. The difficulty here is that the Americans seem to have more than one position. Our delegation is distressingly split. While the State Department, represented by Ambassador James J. Wadsworth, is its nominal head, it is actually a conglomeration of several government agencies, whose interests do not necessarily jibe and, so far, have not been made to do so by the White House, the one authority superior to them all. "Even a wrong policy would be a help as long as it was a single policy," one delegate told me wearily. In the absence of a set of bracing unequivocal instructions, the delegation has contrived a negative, makeshift unity that has often consisted of opposing the Soviet Union merely for the sake of opposing it, by the technique of raising new issue upon new issue. While none of the members of our delegation admit to being against a test-ban agreement, either Adequatist or Perfectionist, two of the bureaus represented on it appear to view any such accomplishment with less relish than their teammates. These are the Atomic Energy Commission and the Department of Defense, and to some extent it could be argued that it is incumbent on them to feel the way they do, since the quality of the country's arsenal is their responsibility. "What better way is there for the Russians to keep us from testing than by engaging us in this marathon talkfest?" one of our military advisers asked me over a café table.

❦

My interview with Tsarapkin, which took place at the Soviet villa, had its disconcerting features.

For one thing, we met not, as I had anticipated, in the Ambassador's office (which, I had been told, was dominated by a photograph of Lenin) but outdoors, under a small portico, where we occupied green wooden benches at a bare table. Nor were we alone. A strapping, curly-haired young man in sunglasses occupied a third bench and used the table for recording our colloquy on a stenographer's pad. He was an unusal stenographer. Occasionally, unasked, he would rephrase the Ambassador's answers to my questions, and his face wore a steady smile that was more confident than friendly. I could not help wondering, as the interview went along, whether he and his pad had been drafted to keep me in line or to keep tabs on Tsarapkin himself. I was unprepared, too, for the view at our feet. It was the villa's flower garden, and its prettiness struck me as incongruous, considering the matters that Tsarapkin and I were there to discuss. The garden was a mass of brilliance, its roses in bloom, its begonia borders baking in the day's hot sun, and framing everything were hedges that had just been trimmed. In the distance lay the French Alps, their peaks unshrouded under a reigning blue sky, and, not far from the villa, the United Nations flag atop the Palais, its pale blue almost matching the sky's, was barely fluttering.

Most disconcerting of all, however, was Tsarapkin himself, and this was not particularly because of anything he said; his remarks, though couched in unlawyerlike language and concerned with topics that were surely of interest to most people, were, as I had expected, consistently tendentious. What impressed me was Tsarapkin's manner. It was always one of urgent conviction, his large head nodding vigorously, his eyes squinting to emphasize a point. I had not observed any such sense of conviction among the American diplomats, but then, unlike Tsarapkin, none of them had a definite (if changeable) party line to cling to.

The treaty should have been signed over a year ago, the Ambassador said as the smiling young man scribbled easily on his stenographer's pad, but certain military and scientific elements in the United States desired to experiment with nuclear weapons. It was an "aggressive" desire, he maintained, but excuses had been invented to make it appear virtuous. For instance, he said, these elements declared that their explosions would not make the atmosphere dirty with fallout, because they would be conducted underground, but they neglected to mention that the resultant radioactivity could conceivably escape into the air above or infiltrate subterranean sources of water. "Scientists have made mistakes before," he observed.

"The day is very hot," the young man announced, and, while Tsarapkin and I paused and watched him, took off his coat. Hunched over his pad again, he indicated that we might resume.

The purpose of these underground tests, Tsarapkin thereupon asserted, was the refinement of nuclear weapons to a point where they could be used tactically in specific military situations, but this was patently "foolish." If a nuclear war ever broke out, he said, his head nodding, America's refined weapons would be answered with, in effect, boorish big bombs.

Then, too, he continued, it was virtuously claimed that these underground tests would improve methods of distinguishing earthquakes from nuclear detonations, but, as he saw it, the tests were concerned less with facilitating detection than with demonstrating new possibilities of concealment. Since these possibilities might be infinite, he said, did that mean that the number of sessions at the Palais also had to be infinite? Or was it that aggressive elements in the United States sought good concealment techniques in order to hold secret tests?

I said I doubted whether any country that had a free press could keep its tests secret.

"Like Project Argus?" Tsarapkin retorted, referring to the American nuclear test in space two years ago that was kept from the public for six months. But, the Ambassador added quickly, he did not want me to think that he was lumping all Americans with their militaristic experimenters; he knew that ordinary Americans and "most of your intelligentsia and scientists" wanted an end to tests.

"How does public opinion in a controlled state like the Soviet Union show itself?" I asked.

Millions of Russians, attending hundreds of after-work meetings in all parts of his country, had protested nuclear tests, Tsarapkin replied.

"Were these meetings organized from the top?"

"Individuals, too, speak out in my country," Tsarapkin said, responding to my question obliquely. "I have received hundreds of letters from individuals who say they have lost a husband or father in one war and do not want to have to live through another war, a nuclear one. Some of these letters are angry with me. They want to know why I have been in Geneva so long without coming to an agreement."

The Ambassador rose, and so did the young man. The interview was over. Before I left, however, Tsarapkin invited me to take a turn in the garden. His voice as he called my attention to its beauties was no longer urgent but chatty and amiable. The young man, who had come along and was walking a few feet behind us, had tucked his stenographer's pad out of sight. When we reached the center of the garden, Tsarapkin and I stood looking into a tiny pool. Goldfish were darting gracefully about in its depths. We watched them in silence for a moment, and then the Ambassador, a broad smile spreading over his face, said, "Those goldfish—it will not be long before they turn to red."

❦

Knottier problems than the few that remain have been solved in the course of the conference, but none have been approached with greater hesitancy, for the solution of these final ones could signify a commitment to test the elasticity of national sovereignty as it has never been tested before. For one thing, the proposed pact would take little account of the sacredness of national boundaries. It would call for a world-wide network of listening posts whose placement would depend not on diplomatic factors but on the location of earthquake areas. Each of these control posts would record "unidentified events" that might be either earthquakes or nuclear blasts. If an "unidentified event" was later found to be "suspicious," an international inspection team of geologists, physicists, drilling experts, and others would be dispatched to the spot from Vienna, the proposed headquarters of the control system, and would search for traces of human activity—in nearby mines, for example—that might indicate a violation of the treaty.

❦

Not every earthquake that occurs would be treated as an "unidentified event." There are too many earthquakes—twenty-eight thousand annually—to make that feasible, and since the great majority of them are far weaker than any disturbance that could result from the weakest nuclear weapon yet devised, it would not be necessary. Even so, the treaty's machinery would be hard pressed to keep up with the "unidentified events" that it would be obliged to investigate, for nearly a thousand earthquakes would fall into this category—all those whose seismic force was roughly the equivalent of the Hiroshima bomb or anything above that. About thirty per cent of such disturbances can be identified by means of present seismological techniques, and there is a good possibility that these techniques will be improved before long. Thanks to the attention focussed on seismology by the conference, I was told, this branch of science, which is still in its Stone Age, is about to receive international recognition of a sort that it has never known. (Our Department of Defense, for example, has appropriated sixty-six million dollars for a two-year study of seismological detection.)

As fate would have it, Geneva itself recently experienced an earthquake whose magnitude, in seismological terms, was approximately that of the Hiroshima bomb. "It wasn't much, but it did wake my wife and me," said the man who told me about it—a member of the Foreign Service who is here with the United States delegation. "It came at midnight, and I felt a lateral thrust and heard a creaking in the wood-and-stucco house we live in. I'd been through this before—in Peru, where I'd served—so I wasn't worried. 'It's an earthquake,' I told my wife, and went back to sleep. The next day, at the Palais, the delegates joked about it. One of us wondered if the Swiss had developed a bomb, and another wanted to know which of our countries had tried a sneak underground test. The earthquake made it easier to get started with the day's session. We don't have too many chances for jokes."

July, 1961

In the past year, the atmosphere at the conference has altered considerably. A year ago, as one member of our delegation put it to me quite unofficially the other day, "the United States was dragging its feet." At that point, as nearly everyone connected with the talks realized, it was the Russians who were pushing the conference forward, providing ideas, granting concessions, and displaying a certain restraint in making propaganda capital of an opponent's singularly wavering conduct. (On one unresolved issue of importance, for example, instructions from Washington took the better part of a year in reaching Geneva, to the chagrin of our delegation and that of Great Britain.) At present, though, thanks to a thorough overhauling of our position by President Kennedy and his advisers, it is the Americans who are forcing the action. In contrast to a year ago, British diplomats here are delighted with our burst of initiative, and are no longer chafing at the faltering ways of their formidable partner. It is the Russians who now appear to be dragging their feet, and Western representatives here are quick to offer evidence that this is not their view alone. It was pointed out to me that organizations given to demonstrating publicly against any use of nuclear arms have recently made the Soviet Union the target of critical remarks; sections of the Japanese press that were formerly hostile toward us are writing appreciatively of our new policies; and a similar shift of sentiment has occurred in India, Sweden, and neutral African countries.

❦

"I think this conference of ours stands a better chance of being remembered if it fails than if it succeeds," a Western delegate told me over dinner at a café near the Rhône. "If it succeeds, it'll very likely lead to other conferences—more sweeping ones that will deal with actual disarming, not merely the halting of explosions. But if it fails—well, we may look back on these talks of ours as a magnificent chance that went to waste. Anyway," he added, shrugging, "one thing that hasn't changed in the past year is the suspicion at the Palais. It's still present at every session, like a virus. Of course, I'm glad we look better this year than we did last, but I sometimes wonder what we'd do if the Russians suddenly took a reasonable line with us. Maybe we'd pull back, we'd get so suspicious. It's probably no accident that we and they haven't been in equally conceding moods at one and the same time."

The initiative that we have gained at the Palais is owed in part to long overdue clarifications of our position and in part to concessions. Among the latter, we are now prepared, with the consent of the British, to let the Russians have a voice in the workings of the treaty that would be equal to that of the United States and Great Britain combined. Thus, the two Western countries, halving their ballots, would be unable to out-vote the Soviet Union on the control commission, the policy-making agency contemplated by the treaty. As a further blandishment to the Russians, the United States and Britain are willing to unmerge themselves and contribute as separate countries to the cost of the detection system, which would be expensive. Its construction, it is estimated, will come to close to two billion dollars, and its annual maintenance to something like three hundred million.

Accommodating though these and other moves might seem, the Russians have their objections. They want the heads of control posts on their soil to be nationals of their own, which, in the view of the United States and England, might make for skulduggery in the relaying of accurate information to the headquarters of the control system. Western sources here are aware that the Soviets want Russians in charge of the posts as a hedge against possible espionage, but any such spies, these same sources add, would have poor working conditions. "The spies wouldn't see much," a British official told me. "These posts have to be in isolated areas, because their equipment is so delicate. The noise of a passing truck, you see, or the pounding of sea waves could mask the readings of the instruments. As far as we're concerned, we don't care if the Russians surround each post with a division of M.V.D. men. We wouldn't be on a very good wicket, though, would we, if we had to think twice about the man who's sending the data?"

One of the oldest disagreements at the Palais concerns the number of annual "on-site inspections," which would be made when a seismic event was suspicious enough to warrant a trip by an inspection team. The Soviet Union is willing to have its domain visited three times for this purpose. We and the British consider this paltry. Depending on the number of seismic events, we want to be able to send inspection teams from twelve to twenty times. The makeup of the inspection teams is another obstacle. The Soviet Union insists that half the members be Russian. The West is equally insistent that this would compromise the very point of an inspection.

❦

Speculating on the causes of Communist suspicion is an almost compulsive guessing game here; any number can play, and it distracts Western delegates from wondering whether the Russians are testing clandestinely. The U-2 incident is sometimes offered as a reason for Soviet mistrust, but this is generally dismissed as superficial. Perhaps, it is guessed, popular discontent inside the Soviet Union is back of Tsarapkin's haggling over control posts and inspection visits, the thought being that outlanders, poking their noses into remote, untouristic places, might foment further unrest. Then there is the "pair-of-shoes" theory, which suggests that the sight of a well-made pair of shoes and other apparel on a foreign control-post technician might give a muzhik subversive ideas. "He who gains power conspiratorially sees the world through a conspirator's eyes," an official said to me. The Communists' xenophobia, it is also ventured, may represent a simple desire to conceal their rampant inefficiency. And, as might be expected, China's relations with the Soviet Union figure in the guessing game. The thinking here—and it is rather widely held—is that the Chinese have urged the Soviet Union to scuttle a test-ban agreement, because it would prevent them from developing nuclear weapons of their own. "This presupposes that the Russians won't give the Chinese bombs," an English conjecturer told me. "I don't believe it." U.S. Ambassador Arthur H. Dean, who has replaced Ambassador Wadsworth, thinks that the southeasterly course of Russia's main rivers has something to do with the way the Soviets act. Lecturing before the International Law Commission here on May 15th, he declared that the rivers kept Russia from experiencing "the development of concepts of international law, which flowed from the interrelationships of Western European kingdoms and principalities within the Western Christian family under the theoretical all-embracing supremacy of the Papacy and under the influence of Roman law, of Greco-Roman civilization, and of trade."

❦

The members of the delegations know as well as most newspaper readers that their conference is at present in a languishing state, and their air of weariness and discouragement is plain to see, from the most junior of them on up to the three Ambassadors—all of whom, incidentally, I talked with at length, catching Mr. Dean just before he left for Washington for "consultations." Some of the delegates, I noticed, have begun to speak of the conference in the past tense. Occasionally, one hears an isolated bit of exhortation, but the voice that utters it is not buoyant. "As long at this conference goes on, it means—if I may paraphrase Sir Edward Grey—that the lights of Europe have not yet gone out," a British negotiator told me. "Who knows?" I was rhetorically asked by an American. "The Russians may come to the Palais tomorrow prepared to take up an issue they've ducked for months. They do that kind of thing, you know, and for no rhyme or reason." Detachment comes hard for the negotiators these days, dismayed as they are at the prospect of their marathon labors' coming to naught. One senior British diplomat, a man of great correctness who had arranged to see me at his villa directly after a Palais session, apologetically turned me over to an aide soon after I arrived. "He's rather upset," the aide explained, after the senior diplomat had left the room. "Tsarapkin has started using Cold War language of late, and he did it again this afternoon. It's a sign of death, my chief reckons, and this conference may well be one of his last posts."

❦

Tsarapkin, too, is weary. It shows in his eyes—narrow, slanting ones that are nevertheless capable of warmth and spirit. His other features admit of no fatigue, his face being a massive crescent of jaw and thick lips and nose, topped by a great head of iron-gray hair—a face, I have been told, that is often the subject of idle portraiture on note pads at the conference table. I talked with him at his quarters in the modest hotel to which he had recently moved. We sat opposite each other at a light-blue kitchen table. He was flanked by his second, P. F. Shakhov, and his press attaché, Y. M. Vorontsov, who doubles as chauffeur of the delegation car. Curtained off from the small room in which we sat was the kitchenette whose facilities had enticed Tsarapkin from the more elegant hotel in which he had previously lived; he had wanted to be able to have tea and a snack at night without the fuss of room service. We were together an hour, during which he smiled, frowned, looked pensive, and, in relaxed moments, spoke of his family. His voice was as earnest and sincere as those of Dean and Sir Michael Wright. It demanded an effort at times to recall that it had sounded the same a year ago.

I asked Tsarapkin how he thought the conference was going.

"The prospects are not bright, but we will do our best to come to an agreement with our partners. One cannot say, as your press does, that the United

States has changed and that all of a sudden the Soviet Union is stubborn. The conference did not begin with your new proposals. It goes back years. We have made more concessions than you. But let us not bury the test-ban conference. Let us consider it within the broad framework of disarmament."

"And what about controls?" I asked.

"You wish to speak of inspections," Tsarapkin said resignedly. "That number twenty! It means hundreds of millions of dollars. Why? Three inspections are enough. Your government is always suspicious. Is it possible that a great country like yours or mine would seek to make clandestine tests? From the military point of view, the profit would be negligible, and in terms of prestige the country that was caught doing such a thing would lose forever. People all over the world would make an uproar like Jericho—the walls would come tumbling down. No," Tsarapkin said, shaking his head, "do not be so suspicious. Let us simply have an observed peace—a *pactis servans usum.*"

"It is Latin," Vorontsov said.

I asked Tsarapkin if he thought that inspection teams should include citizens of the country that was being inspected.

"Of course," he replied. "Otherwise, who will believe the report if both sides are not represented?"

A year ago, I reminded the Ambassador, he had said that he was receiving a good deal of mail from Soviet citizens who were anxious about the test-ban conference. Was this still the case?

"The letters are not so much now," Tsarapkin

said. "I do not know why." He looked puzzled a moment. "Perhaps people have become used to no more explosions. Perhaps they have begun to think that such things cannot happen again."

❦

Whatever its outcome, the conference seems to have laid to rest the idea that the presence of scientists at a political meeting brings a peerless objectivity to bear in disposing of the agenda. It was an unfair idea, to begin with, but it arose here because the conference followed hard on the heels of a report issued by a group of American, British, Soviet, and other scientists who had been designated by their governments to determine whether a test-ban system of detection was technically feasible. It was only after this group, known as the Committee of Experts to Study the Possibility of Detecting Violations of a Possible Agreement on the Suspension of Nuclear Tests, came in with an affirmative conclusion that the Conference on the Discontinuance of Nuclear Weapons Tests was called. The new conference seemed rigged for success, particularly since scientists would be sitting in on its sessions here as well as at policy-making discussions in Washington, London, and Moscow. A posse of answer men, it was widely thought at the time, had come to the rescue with their sense of method, their data, their aversion to politicking.

Things haven't quite worked out that way. This has not come about because the scientists associated—officially or unofficially—with the conference have failed to emerge as answer men. The difficulty, it appears, has been that they provide too many answers, none of them final. "Scientists like to say that they deal strictly in hard facts," a British diplomat told me somewhat irritatedly. "Well, it's been my experience that they have a distinct talent for softening facts. You listen to them one day about space testing or seismology or whatnot, and the next day they've got hold of some new data and have changed their minds. Or else, hard facts or no, they're in complete disagreement with each other, like doctors arguing about whether to operate on a patient. It's simply not the sort of advice on which to base a political treaty."

"It's in the nature of science to guess," a physicist here informed me cheerfully, "and it doesn't matter if you guess wrong. You think nothing of it. But it's different with politicians. They want to guess correctly all the time, which seems odd, since they negotiate with people, who, thank goodness, don't behave like inanimate matter. Scientists go into science to escape people," he added, guessing intrepidly. "Now we find ourselves stuck with them."

By now, it is perfectly clear—as it should have been in 1958—that scientists are not destined to take the gamble out of politics. That remains intact—a conglomerate of suspicion, fast dealing, power plays, and wary idealism. But since 1958 the scientists, I gathered from some of them here, have come to perceive, for better or worse, their expected role at the Palais. It calls on them to recognize the conference as a thoroughly political event—almost as though nucleonics were of little moment to its proceedings. While they may have political notions—because, like diplomats, they possess such inexact attributes as interest, intelligence, and ingenuity—the political culmination of their technical education lies in providing data (subject to change) with which diplomats may evaluate risks. "Political questions are our department," a U.S. Foreign Service man here told me. "Such questions have to do with a willingness to take risks. Three inspections or twenty in Russia? How many control posts there—fifteen or nineteen? It's the scientists who tell us the dimensions of these risks, but when it comes to decisions—unscientific guesses, if you will—that's where we negotiators, and perhaps the governments we represent, stand or fall."

❦

On May 30th, at the conference's three hundred and twelfth meeting, Ambassador Dean, addressing his Soviet counterpart, likened a test-ban agreement to "anticipatory disarmament." He pressed home the idea that thermonuclear weapons would never have been developed had there been a test-ban treaty ten years ago. "Our situation today is very similar," Dean told Tsarapkin. "We at this table today do not actually know what advanced developments in nuclear weaponry might be prevented if we three countries were to conclude a nuclear test-ban treaty. . . . Without it, or some other disarmament agreement, there will undoubtedly be even more serious disarmament problems ten years hence."

The Ambassador's thought implies a limit to human wisdom in dealing with its own inventions. The proceedings at the Palais thus far would seem to lend it plausibility.

July, 1962

The Russians resumed nuclear testing last September and may begin a new series of explosions next month, but, nevertheless, a feeling exists among the diplomats that all is not yet necessarily lost. This feeling, one gathers, is based not so much on any specific progress at the negotiating table as on the fact that the test-ban talks, which have been dragging on for four years, are now in a state of ferment—that is to say, alive. Ideas are in the air, I was told by a diplomat who has attended the talks from their inception. Last summer, the negotiators were snarling or yawning, but that has changed since testing started again. The negotiators are not as worried as they were about being tricked, and, it seems to me, they are less frustrated and more treaty-minded. Since March, the delegations of Great Britain, the United States, and the Soviet Union have been deliberating as a subcommittee of a seventeen-nation group formed by the United Nations and known as the Committee on Disarmament. As a subcommittee, the three nuclear powers have been continuing their search for a test-ban treaty, while the committee as a whole devotes its attention to a full-scale disarmament. This, of course, does not make the negotiations of the three any less important. On the contrary, it is argued here that the present arrangement has the effect of emphasizing the subcommittee's work; in the context of the full committee's examination of the possibilities of disarmament—of doing away with the tools of war, of dismantling military establishments—the relatively minor goal of halting tests emerges more clearly than ever as the first step in slowing up the arms race. "Whenever I talk to people about disarmament, it's always the test-ban treaty they bring me around to," I was told by Joseph B. Godber, Great Britain's Minister of State, who has taken Sir Michael's place here as his country's chief negotiator. "It's something they can understand. It has to do with the here and now, and they want an end to this fouling of the air they breathe."

Beyond the depressing prospect of the Soviets' Arctic shots—or of additional American shots in the Pacific—lies the test-ban conference's oldest and most persistent difficulty: the distrust, justified or not, that follows every move made by the Soviet Union on the one side and by the United States and Great Britain on the other. This is probably most strongly exemplified by the question of whether a test-ban treaty would give an international commission of scientists the right to inspect the territory of a country in which a suspicious seismic event had been detected, and to identify the occurrence as either a clandestine test or an earthquake. "On-site inspections are crucial to any treaty," Ambassador Dean told me. "There is a difference between detection and identification. The one is simply the registering of an event, the other—identification—is the nailing down, the analysis, the verification of exactly what happened. Certainly, we're always learning more about seismology, but even the most enthusiastic researchers grant that we're years away from being able to know for sure the precise cause of a suspicious event without the necessity of a field trip. I suppose it's comparable to a heart examination. When a cardiogram picks up something in a patient, that's only the beginning for a reputable doctor. He won't stop until he's found out just what's back of the patient's condition. Maybe it's nothing—possibly just a fading battery in the doctor's equipment—or maybe it's something serious that needs action."

❦

Tsarapkin has been replaced as Russia's chief delegate by Deputy Foreign Minister Valerian A. Zorin, and Zorin was no less certain than Dean of his country's position when I spoke with him in the small, musty living room of his villa, cluttered with old-fashioned, comfortable furniture and dominated by a large bust of Lenin. An interpreter was with us—a bespectacled earnest young man of perhaps thirty whose English Zorin occasionally corrected. The Deputy Foreign Minister, who vaguely resembles the late William Randolph Hearst, told me that the Soviet Union was not prepared to grant in principle the right of inspection to any international commission of scientists—a reversal of the previous party line. However, he added, his government has no objection to the gathering of data by national detection systems. Detection devices don't need passports, he remarked. He wanted me to understand that Russian scientists, like their American colleagues, were constantly improving the sensitivity of their detection apparatus. "We detected all the underground tests made in New Mexico and Nevada," he said. "So did the French and the Swedes." I asked why his government opposed investigations by an international commission, and he said, not quite answering the question, "We are convinced that the United States is insisting on such types of control for one of two motives—either to commit espionage or to avoid a treaty." When I inquired whether Soviet citizens knew about the effects of fallout, he said that they did. Public opinion in his country, he assured me, was alert to the dangers of nuclear war. Even before the recent World Congress for General Disarmament and Peace in early July in Moscow, he said, meetings against tests had been held in factories and on collective farms, and conferences of "defenders of peace" had been held in every Soviet republic. I asked why the Soviet Union made no announcement of its tests to its own people, and Zorin thought for a moment. "We do not indulge in commotions," he finally said. "The United States describes its tests in order to prepare Americans for more tests. But we are different. We do not wish to make our people nervous."

❦

Naturally, the feeling of hope that I have found here is expressed in guarded terms and tones. But it *is* expressed, and apparently for two reasons. One is the improvement of detection devices, which Ambassador Dean touched on in talking with me. Some people here entertain visions of a day when a purely technological keeping of the peace will be possible. The greater the reliability of detection devices in distinguishing tests from earthquakes, they reason, the more academic becomes the question of territorial inspection. They expect that, thanks in large part to the research efforts of the Department of Defense, the United States will soon modify its demands for inspection rights. The other source of hope is people, not machines. Specifically, it is the influence that is being exerted on the subcommittee by the eight non-aligned countries who are members of the seventeen-nation disarmament group—Brazil, Burma, Ethiopia, India, Mexico, Nigeria, Sweden, and the United Arab Republic. The Eight, as they are sometimes called here, have their differences, political and otherwise, but they do seem to have got together on the proposition that nuclear weapons must not be tested. The interest that the Eight have taken in the subcommittee's work means that the United States, England, and Russia, mired in their moves and countermoves since 1958, at last have a referee. The development is one for which Eastern and Western delegates are thankful. Indeed, there is an almost fable-like quality in the power of the Eight's powerlessness—in the dependence of lions on mice. "You keep sounding off on the same topic for four years, as we have, and you need to be reminded why you're here," a junior American official told me. "That's what these non-aligned countries are doing for us. It's as though the public had its lobby looking over our shoulders. And let's not be complicated about it—it's public opinion that has kept our talks going this long. The fear of testing is the same everywhere, you know, whether it's the knowledgeable fear of a Foreign Minister or the instinctive fear of a mother with a baby carriage picketing the U.N. building." And James Barrington, the permanent secetary of Burma's Foreign Office, said to me, "It's no accident, in my opinion, that the great powers are letting us speak up. They could use all kinds of pressures on us, I suppose, but they haven't used them, for which they deserve credit. The testers are aware that they need a bridge between their positions. They know that the situation is getting out of control. Their discoveries are beginning to frighten them. We eight countries have learned, among other things, what poor business practice the arms race is. The immense investments required are out of all proportion to the efficiency that can be got out of a new weapon. Our group knows that both East and West realize this, but each isn't sure that the other does."

❦

At the moment, a joint memorandum got up by the Eight on April 16th seems to be the driving force behind the talks; scarcely a subcommittee session goes by without its being mentioned. The document, which is less than two pages long, describes itself as "an earnest appeal to the nuclear powers to persist in their efforts to come as soon as possible to an agreement prohibiting nuclear-weapon testing for all time." It proposes the establishment of an international commission of scientists, possibly drawn from nonaligned nations, who would have access to all data collected by independent national detection systems; if such data indicated a suspicious seismic upheaval, the commission would be "invited" to make an inspection of the disturbed area.

There is another proposal inspired by a neutral that has aroused serious discussion here. This is the idea of setting a date on which both sides, having had time for more tests, would call it quits. Despite all the interest that the idea has stirred up, the man responsible for it views it with mixed feelings, as I discovered in a talk with him. He is Dr. Luis Padilla-Nervo, the Mexican Ambassador to the United Nations and the president of the U.N.'s Disarmament Committee, a short, black-haired man in his middle years who studied law at an American university. The cutoff date he is pushing for would be sometime in 1963. "The sooner the better," he told me, nodding emphatically. "Perhaps my idea can bring an end to this disgraceful business, but it is sad, is it not, that one must offer a thought such as mine. It is a recognition of the fear and suspicion that must be satisfied, of the mirage of a lasting military advantage with which the great powers deceive themselves. So now it is the Russians who are about to test, and President Kennedy is surely under pressure from his military men and scientists to do the same. 'A fifty-megaton bomb the size of a football must be found,' the military men say. And the scientists say that the tests harm us no more than our wristwatches or our chest X-rays, but do they really know what they are doing to us and to our great-great-grandchildren? I do not like the fact that the idea I have presented here in Geneva permits the spread of more such harm, no matter how limited. But it is an endless process that seems to be going on. Each side accuses the other of being the first to test, but we no longer want to know who was the first. We want to know who will be the last."

Postscript

Nuclear tests—atmospheric ones—did come to a halt in 1963, but not because of Padilla-Nervo's plan. In fact, no specific plan appears to have produced this signal development. It occurred on August 5, 1963, when the foreign ministers of Great Britain, Russia, and the United States assembled with their retinues in a Kremlin ballroom and signed a partial test-ban treaty—partial in that it banned tests in the atmosphere, in space, and underwater, but not underground. The pact, signed a few hours before the eighteenth anniversary of the Hiroshima attack, was widely hailed as a potential forerunner of disarmament itself, and while this may prove to be the case, it is no certainty. The long-range effects of the treaty are hard to predict, for immediate political concerns had much to do with its enactment. The Russians, for example, were extremely mindful of their ideological struggle with their Chinese comrades; to the Russians, the agreement may have seemed tailored to set off their policy of coexistence in a "peace-loving" light, as opposed to the truculence of Peking's implacable leftism. As for American political exigencies, these were largely taken care of by our refusal to ban underground tests; in the absence of an on-site inspection system, few congressional and military figures were prepared to support the treaty without the partial continuation of our weapons program. This play of political expediency left some people with misgivings. The same element of expediency, they felt, that had made possible the treaty could just as easily bring about its undoing. Politics, it appeared to them, had served a magnificent cause without magnificence—but then, it could be asked, wasn't that the way good things often got done? Political leaders, it might be argued, sometimes behave with more stature than they realize, depending on the fundamental rightness of their acts, and perhaps the test-ban treaty is a case in point. However shrewd the reasons for its ratification, none of its signatories can again dare to befoul air and milk without a great public outcry. As of now, the treaty stands as a monument to the efficacy of continual negotiation.

After its adoption, there were no explosions in the atmosphere until October 16, 1964, when the People's Republic of China tested its first atomic bomb in Sinkiang Province. At the time, British, American, and Russian negotiators were preparing to resume their work on completing the partial treaty. Their sessions continue to be held at the Palais, as they have been for the better part of a decade.

4
A Scientist's Advice

The partial test-ban treaty was an outgrowth of a point of view that had been voiced for a number of years by scientists and non-scientists alike in many countries. Among American scientists, an early proponent of general arms control was Dr. Jerome B. Wiesner, who was scientific adviser to President Kennedy at the time the treaty was signed in Moscow. The following is an account of Dr. Wiesner's day-to-day activities in that government post as well as of the development of his outlook on arms control. Parts of the account were written in the present tense, and I have left them this way, the better to preserve some of the atmosphere of the Kennedy Administration.

While most of us have in the last few years come to recognize the momentous interplay between scientific achievements and world politics, not many people are as keenly aware of it as a restless, resourceful forty-seven-year-old professor of electrical engineering on leave of absence from the Massachusetts Institute of Technology named Jerome Bert Wiesner, who is President Kennedy's Special Assistant for Science and Technology. Wiesner's life has been centered on that interplay since he was appointed to his present office, directly after President Kennedy's inauguration, and for the past two years his large, black-thatched head has been buzzing with Presidential questions about the country's trimness as a scientific force—a trimness in which the government invests about fourteen billion dollars a year. Wiesner's opinions come to light in a variety of circumstances. They may be expressed at a White House conclave, resplendent with military uniforms, in which the relative capabilities of different weapons are being debated, since Wiesner is an expert on the subject of ballistic missiles. Or perhaps, since he is also an expert on disarmament, the President wants to know his estimation of a new type of seismograph—a detection device that may contribute to a comprehensive nuclear-test-ban treaty—in which case Wiesner may put forth his views before a meeting attended by officials of the government's Arms Control and Disarmament Agency. If a post of scientific importance is to be filled, it is Wiesner who is likely to suggest suitable candidates to the President and the appropriate department head, by memo or telephone. The teaching of science, too, is a matter on which the Professor often expresses his ideas at White House meetings, for the Chief Executive is disturbed by the fact that current methods of instruction are generally outmoded. More than once, sitting alone with Mr. Kennedy, the scientist has set forth at length his conception of a reasonable approach to the exploration of space. And plummeting vicariously to the bottom of the sea, the President and his Special Assistant have at other times pondered our future moves in oceanography, a domain of knowledge about which the United States is growing increasingly curious, for reasons having to do with defense and the enrichment of our diet, among other things. Not so long ago, the two men talked over the wisdom of building and launching an expensive oceanographic vessel—a research ship whose crew of specialists would roam the oceans in no particular hurry, stopping whenever they chose, to sound the depths for their secrets. It is possible that, as they talked on, the vision of this unhurried ship gave them a certain respite from their more burdensome tasks, for both men are passionate sailors.

In periods when the interplay between science and politics is especially intense or complex, Wiesner may be in and out of the President's office three or four times a day, and on occasion the two may confer at the edge of the White House pool. Like other close aides, Wiesner is almost never beyond Mr. Kennedy's reach. Whenever he is away from his desk, in the Executive Offices of the White House, he leaves a list of the phone numbers at which he can be reached; he gets about in a government car that is driven by a chauffeur and is equipped with two-way radio, over which White House operators can call him while he is in transit. His home in Chevy Chase is furnished with a government safe, in which, before turning in, he stores documents that he has studied during the evening. On summer weekends, he sometimes hitches a flight to New England with Mr. Kennedy, aboard the Presidential jet. After the plane lands at Otis Air Force Base, near Falmouth, the President goes on by helicopter to Hyannis Port and Wiesner goes on by car and ferry to Martha's Vineyard, where he has a summer house. If the phone isn't ringing for him when he reaches his island home, he may go sailing on Menemsha Pond in an eighteen-foot boat that he owns. It has no ship-to-shore communications equipment, but Wiesner cannot delude himself that he has finally got away from it all. At any moment, a cutter from the Coast Guard station at Menemsha may bear down on his small craft with an important message. It would not be an ideal time—what time would?—for him to learn of a national emergency, but, unlike many other people, he would know exactly what to do if one should arise. His orders call for him to make his way to the President's side.

Though Wiesner has such easy access to the President, and though his advice is sought by Cabinet members as well, he is no gray eminence ruling our scientific roost. He has his influence, to be sure, but his recommendations are not always acted upon, any more than are those of other Presidential advisers, including the Cabinet members themselves. Naturally, he doesn't relish setbacks, but since he is free of any tendency to confuse wisdom with infallibility, they don't leave him unduly ruffled. In fact, Wiesner suspects that he would find it unsettling if he always had his own way, since science, crucial as it is, is only one of a complex of factors shaping the international scene. There is no isolating its role, he maintains, and he cites the presence of a scientist in the White House as clear evidence of that fact. (Two men preceded him in the adviser's post, which was founded in 1957 by President Eisenhower—Dr. James R. Killian, President of M.I.T. at the time, and Dr. George Kistiakowski, a Harvard chemist.) Wiesner doubts whether there has ever really been a neat line of demarcation between science and world affairs; he thinks it would be nice if there were, but since there isn't, one of his regular tasks is to elucidate technical reports for the President's, and perhaps the public's, political consideration. "The phrase 'political science' doesn't mean what it used to," he says. "It's become a double-entendre."

As the President's Special Assistant, Wiesner finds himself incessantly shuttling across the mythical border between science and politics and being pulled this way or that as he considers such matters as the budgeting of weapons development, the choice of medicines for the dispensaries of new African republics, the needs of pure research and the needs of backward American industries, and the performance of the latest Russian rockets. It is not an orderly agenda, but Wiesner, a reflective, quiet-spoken man, is able to deal with it quite calmly. One reason for this—so friends of his have suggested—is that Wiesner happens to have a high regard for political figures, at least in the abstract. He is impressed, it seems, with the responsibility they are willing to bear, particularly when they are confronted by problems that call for some knowledge of science. "In reaching decisions, technical data, no matter how clear and simple, can help them only up to a point," he has said. "In the end, they have to fall back on instinct—a flash of intuition—and, with the stakes as high as they are nowadays, that takes courage." Wiesner has claimed that he isn't put off even by the average politician's preoccupation with appropriations and parochial interests. "Of course, a politician is out to please the voters, and why shouldn't he be? After all, who else is it that's affected by the government?" he once remarked to an old M.I.T. colleague who was down from Cambridge. Wiesner's government service has convinced him that a scientist in Washington, or any other capital, must remember that he is a long way from the laboratory and the scientific method. The laboratory is certainly Wiesner's spiritual home, and the scientific method—the acquisition of facts and their arrangement, by inspiration, into harmonious, predictable patterns—is something he has never ceased to revere. "The scientific method is the rejection of shadow for substance, of dilemma for solution," he has told science students. "It represents nothing less than the good manners of the mind. I believed this before I came to Washington, and I will still believe it after I've left."

❦

President Kennedy undoubtedly had a number of reasons for choosing Wiesner as his scientific adviser, but possibly the strongest one was the fact that he had already sampled the quality of the M.I.T. professor's advice. Wiesner, that is, was pre-tested. During the 1960 campaign, the politician frequently called upon the scientist to assist him in developing Democratic positions on certain issues relating to war and peace—issues that the two men were to continue discussing, in a setting of vast power and responsibility. "Senator Kennedy couldn't easily have found a better man to fill his needs," Dr. Jerrold R. Zacharias, a well-known physics professor at M.I.T., has said, recalling the campaign. "Their styles were so similar; both of them were young, tireless, and tough-minded, and both went to the heart of any situation with a kind of automatic speed. Furthermore, the Senator had Jerry's whole background in military problems to draw upon. Jerry was soaked in those problems. Since 1942, he'd had a hand in submarine warfare, air defense, atom bombs, guerrilla warfare, civil defense, and psychological warfare." The campaign, with its daily turmoil, gave Senator Kennedy and Wiesner plenty of opportunities to get to know each other, and apparently they hit it off, for a few weeks after Election Day the President-elect, to the surprise of no one in his entourage, invited Wiesner to join the new administration. Wiesner, however, did not accept immediately but discussed the matter with the President-elect on two occasions. He had reservations, and not until Mr. Kennedy said that he was already aware of them, and still wanted him, did Wiesner agree to take the job.

Wiesner did not hesitate on the ground of personal inconvenience, though he might well have. Accepting the assignment would mean giving up his job at M.I.T., which included the directorship of the Institute's Research Laboratory of Electronics, one of the world's great centers of communications research; it would mean uprooting his wife and four children from a comfortable old sixteen-room house in Watertown, a pleasant, unfashionable township near Cambridge; it would mean cutting his annual income as a professor and an industrial consultant nearly in half; and it would mean unloading shares in several profitable electronics firms, one of which he had helped found. What bothered him, however, was an altogether different consideration: the thought that he might turn out to be a political liability. He had engaged in disarmament activities, both as a government delegate to international conferences and as a private citizen, and he feared that these activities might represent a kind of "past" that would hurt the incoming administration. "That word 'disarmament'—it's pretty suspect," Wiesner once remarked. "It has come to mean 'softness,' 'unpreparedness,' 'appeasement.' Everybody says he's for disarmament, but discuss it as a serious hope and you're likely to be patronized as 'unrealistic.' It's hard to believe, but self-preservation has become a controversial issue."

Wiesner's disarmament "past" dated, essentially, from 1958, and came after sixteen years of heavy involvement with military research, yet his concern with arms control was not that of a previously aloof scientist who suddenly acquires a social conscience. Wiesner, according to his friends, had always had one. If anything, they say, his disarmament activities were simply one stage in a continuing quest to satisfy his social conscience. Because he found the new world into which he had thrust himself a highly stimulating one, he went at these activities with great drive, but then the same drive had marked his rise to eminence in the scientific world. "When something lays hold of Jerry's interest, he gives himself to it a hundred and fifty per cent," Professor Elting Morison, a noted M.I.T. historian, has observed. "He's a moral man, in my opinion, and that may account for his strong sense of commitment." In Wiesner's own opinion, his deep interest in arms control owed its origin primarily neither to his social conscience nor to his instinct for self-preservation—though both no doubt had something to do with it—but to his study of arms themselves. Only after Wiesner had become thoroughly acquainted with America's offensive and defensive systems did he come to the conclusion that arms alone could not guarantee security. His decision was not accompanied by any dramatic denunciation of weapons as vile and evil. It simply reflected a comprehension—gradual, careful, almost occupational—that no matter how ingenious and elaborate military defenses became, they could never become impregnable. The more he learned of military needs, he has said, the more hopeless the possibility of ever satisfying them appeared. Other scientists versed in military research have arrived at similar conclusions. One of them is Dr. Harold Brown, the Director of Defense Research and Engineering for the Department of Defense. "The more powerful the weapons that a nation possesses, the more insecure it feels," Dr. Brown once told an interviewer.

Wiesner does not think of himself as having undergone a "conversion." In his view, he had been as much concerned with preventing the outbreak of war when he was developing weapons as when he was speaking up at a disarmament meeting. The public might not readily understand this, he realized, but scientists with a background in weapons would; indeed, he saw such scientists as being in a special position to do something about the control of arms, simply because they were acquainted with the arms that had to be controlled. The fact of the matter is, Wiesner has said, that a close connection exists between the technical nature of weapons and the limitation of weapons, and no arms-control arrangement is likely to get anywhere unless it makes use of the military researcher's knowledge. Wiesner's own work as a military researcher—in radar, rockets, bombs, and submarines—has earned him the respect of military men. "Jerry is a hardheaded man of tremendous technical competence, and the Polaris program owes him a big debt," Vice Admiral William Raborn, Deputy Chief of Naval Operations for Development, has declared, and General Bernard A. Schriever, commander of the Air Force Systems Command, has said of Wiesner, "He's unquestionably been one of the greatest contributors to this nation's strength since the war." In the fall of 1957, however, another Air Force general, a famous hero of the last war, saw fit to charge Wiesner with impracticality. Pounding his Pentagon desk, he told the scientist, "Stop trying to sell me on missiles! They'll have no value in your lifetime or mine!" Four days later, the Russians put Sputnik in orbit.

❦

Like most of his friends, Wiesner had expected to stick to the academic life after the war, but the truculence of the Soviet Union gradually aroused his curiosity about the state of our defenses. When he looked into it, he discovered weaknesses so glaring that to neglect them, he felt, was to invite war. "In the middle fifties, we were definitely yielding the initiative in military technology to the Russians," he has said. The result was that he lent himself to a long succession of military projects, each of which seemed at the time to supply a missing piece in some necessary mosaic of might. Many of these pieces are integral parts of our defense system today. One of the projects led to the creation of our Distant Early Warning network, which might not have materialized without Wiesner's research on the scatter propagation of radio waves. Another was Project Hartwell, a Navy study in which Wiesner and a number of other scientists devised methods of coping with submarine attacks. Still another was Project Charles, an Air Force study, begun not long after the Russians acquired thermonuclear weapons, that was designed to overhaul our air defenses. A fourth, Project Teapot, was organized at a time when most American scientists and military men were skeptical about the feasibility of intercontinental ballistic missiles. Our intelligence reports indicated Russian activity in this field, however, so the Air Force decided that it should seek definitive advice on the matter. It thereupon rounded up a committee of top-flight scientists, headed by the late Dr. John Von Neumann, a leading mathematician, who later became a member of the Atomic Energy Commission, and including Wiesner. A great deal hung on the committee's judgment, both because the country's safety might be at stake and because our basic military outlook might have to be revamped. After intensive study, the committee delivered its verdict: intercontinental ballistic missiles were indeed feasible, and we had better get on with a crash program. "That committee's work was a turning point in getting this country started in ballistic missiles," General Schriever has told an acquaintance.

It was in 1957, Wiesner has said, that he saw

that Project This and Project That weren't sufficient to produce any lasting pattern of security. In that year, President Eisenhower appointed a panel of sixty scientists and non-scientists, under the chairmanship of the late H. Rowan Gaither, Jr., chairman of the board of the Ford Foundation, to study the relative effectiveness of active and passive air defense. Wiesner was technical director of the Gaither panel, and he and his colleagues put in six months of hard research. The findings of the panel, and even its formal title, have remained secret to this day, but their general features have often been publicly discussed. Before it was through, the group had made an exhaustive investigation of the impact of nuclear war, real or threatened, on the United States. "The panel gave me my first look at the complete military package," Wiesner has said. "The studies I'd been associated with before that had been on the antiseptic side, since they were limited to comparing the capabilities of a particular American weapon with those of a foreign model." The panel looked into the possibility of a nationwide shelter program, but it went much further, considering such things as the biological effects of radiation; the effects of biological warfare; food, fuel, and medical needs in the event of nuclear war; methods of preventing looting during and after attacks; and even the likely outlines of postwar civilization. An emergency, the panel foresaw, might well bring about garrison-state measures, including absolute government control over industry and labor and travel. It estimated the cost of an effective air-defense system and of an effective civil-defense system, and though these figures have never been released, they are known to have been astronomical. Even so, they were arrived at on the assumption that the Soviet Union would not continue to improve its military machine, and this was no more likely than that the American military machine would remain static. When President Eisenhower heard the findings of the Gaither study, he told members of the panel, "Gentlemen, you have left out only one thing. Where are the bulldozers we'll need for scraping the bodies off the streets?"

One of the most profound impressions that the Gaither study made on Wiesner became fully clear to him only with the passage of time. During their researches, he and the other panel members relied heavily on intelligence assessments of Russian capabilities. "Some of my colleagues and I came to realize that, given the secrecy of the Soviet Union, these assessments were largely imaginary," Wiesner has said. "We exaggerated Russian capabilities and so we exaggerated the responses we had to make. Thinking back on my work with the panel, I came to understand that we were in an arms race not only with the Russians but with ourselves as well. The Russians were caught in the same trap. The thought was inescapable that the more either side tried to buy security, the tighter the trap became."

❦

It was not long after the Gaither study was completed that Wiesner plunged into the problem of disarmament, and, from the start, his most demanding activities in this new field were those he undertook for the government. They sometimes kept him away from his laboratory and home for weeks at a time. One such assignment took him to Geneva in the fall of 1958, as technical director of a sixty-man United States delegation to the Conference on the Prevention of Surprise Attack, which was attended by representatives of nine other powers—Russia, Poland, Czechoslovakia, Rumania, Albania, Italy, France, Canada, and Britain. "Jerry knew the capabilities of every one of us American delegates—exactly what each of us could do when it came to preparing position papers for our various panels," William A. Higinbotham, head of the Instrumentation Division of the Brookhaven National Laboratory, who was a fellow-delegate, has told a friend. "He probably knew as much about the members of the other delegations. Whenever he went to lunch or to a café, it was in the company of a Russian or a Pole whose point of view he believed it important to understand." As for the conference itself, it failed, obviously, since the possibility of a surprise attack is still with us. Wiesner felt, however, that the sessions he attended, which were held behind closed doors at the Palais des Nations, yielded a fair amount of solid information. In the course of the meetings, he and hundreds of other delegates weighed the technical aspects of preventing surprise attacks. They presented lengthy papers on the types of weapons most likely to be used in such attacks and the methods of inspecting such weapons; they discussed the matter of ground and aerial observers, whose primary task would be to look out for military build-ups; and they agreed that if the arms race went on unabated, sufficient manpower could never be found to guarantee a foolproof system of inspection against surprise attacks. The delegates also agreed on a good many other aspects of the problem, but the conference finally broke up in a melee of political bickering over the best method of outlawing surprise attacks. The Russians wanted the reduction of stockpiles of weapons; the French concentrated on control of missiles; and the Americans favored President Eisenhower's Open Skies policy, together with ground observation. Those weeks in Geneva had given Wiesner his first close look at an international conference, and he came away feeling that he had been educated, if not elevated. "The conference was a try—good, bad, or indifferent—that had to be made before anyone could make a better one," he has since said.

Each of Wiesner's other government assignments left him with some new reflection on the tortuous course of disarmament. In the spring of 1958, President Eisenhower had appointed him to the President's Science Advisory Committee, and not long afterward a panel of committee members, including Wiesner, began meeting periodically in the White House, in secrecy, to examine the chances of working out an international pact to end the testing of missiles. The aim was narrow, perhaps, but it was important; if governments gave up testing missiles, it was reasoned, they might hesitate to try missile strikes, because the accurate delivery of the warheads would be too uncertain. For several months, Wiesner and the others wrestled with the many technical questions raised by their study, but in the end political reality defeated their efforts. No matter how much headway they might make with technical questions, there was no getting around the fact that at that particular time the Soviet Union appeared to hold a sizable lead over us in ballistic-missiles development, which meant that we could not propose a missile-test moratorium without either appearing weak or asking for a humiliating rebuff. The scientists quietly left the capital, having absorbed what they gathered was a political axiom: When an imbalance of forces exists, a situation is not objectively negotiable. "The President never made our ideas public, they were so clearly doomed to failure," Wiesner has said of these talks.

The following year, Wiesner was back in Washington for another White House meeting, this time as chairman of a panel composed of some members of the Science Advisory Committee and various military men and diplomats—a dozen men all told—which took up the subject of arms control in general instead of limiting itself to a specific issue like missile tests or surprise attacks. At the time the panel was set up, international tensions were relatively low, and it was this condition of vague quiet that led President Eisenhower to decide that a rare moment was at hand for taking stock of the general direction, if any, in which we were moving in the matter of arms control, and, in particular, of the degree of skill with which we were doing so. Wiesner was all for the President's idea. "The international conferences so far had shown that our delegations didn't have adequate technical preparation for carrying on their discussions," he has said. "As for the Russians, they were even worse prepared, so, quite apart from wisdom, simple efficiency was needed at the negotiating table. Certainly it's nice to want arms control, but that's not enough—you also have to know how to go about trying to get it." Over the next five months, Wiesner and his panel met from time to time in the capital, in order to build up a fund of useful knowledge on which the government could draw in future negotiations on arms control. (One beneficiary of this fund of knowledge has been the Arms Control and Disarmament Agency, which was set up by President Kennedy as a new government organization in September, 1961, with William C. Foster as its head.) Among the subjects that the panel, which made periodic secret reports to the President, discussed were problems of international law, the use of international armies, theories of disarmament, the inspection of weapons and the factories in which they were made, and the relationship between the gradual reduction of military forces, or "phasing," and disarmament. Wiesner concedes that the effects of the panel's work are, by their nature, difficult to trace, but he does feel that the quality of the discussions at subsequent international conferences has shown an improvement. And he thinks the panel's activities were significant in another way. "The important thing was that the President saw fit to have the panel organized," he has said. "The government was saying, in effect, that the issue of disarmament was here to stay."

Before Wiesner took over his present job, his

disarmament activities as a private citizen also consumed a good deal of his time. With other learned Cambridge men—Harvard and M.I.T. teachers, mostly—he participated in informal seminars designed to probe the dilemmas of the arms race as well as other issues. Now and then, he appeared on television forums—thoughtful, unsensational programs concerned with the prospect of megaton-bomb attack. He did some writing, too, contributing a foreword and a paper to a special, four-hundred-page issue of *Dædalus,* the quarterly journal of the American Academy of Arts and Sciences, that was published in the fall of 1960 and was devoted to arms control. Wiesner was chairman of the guest editorial board for the issue, and among the contributors were men of various viewpoints, including Dr. Edward Teller; Henry A. Kissinger, Professor of Government at Harvard; Erich Fromm, the psychoanalyst; Senator Hubert H. Humphrey, of Minnesota; and Arthur Larson, a special consultant to President Eisenhower. The issue, which has become a reference work for students of disarmament, probably constitutes the most definitive collection of papers on the subject yet printed. It has been translated into five languages, brought out as a book, under the title "Arms Control, Disarmament, and National Security," by a New York publisher, and distributed as a dividend by the Book-of-the-Month Club.

Wiesner's own paper in that issue of *Dædalus* was one of the longest, and showed the care that had gone into his thinking about the role of international suspicion in disarmament. He considered ways of verifying the truthfulness of the reports made by inspectors under any arms-control systems that might be established. The inspectors themselves might have to be inspected, he wrote, perhaps by means of lie-detector tests; he also put forward the possibility of rewarding ordinary citizens everywhere who disclosed violations of treaty agreements. And he noted that if the Communists were unduly suspicious of the West, the West could also harbor a good deal of suspicion. "The fear of Soviet duplicity is so great among some Western experts who participate in disarmament planning that it is not possible to visualize a level of inspection which would alleviate this fear," he wrote. His foreword, however, ended on a hopeful note: "I am confident that if the nations of the world were to devote one quarter of the effort in terms of manpower and money now being expended in the arms race on the quest for a lasting peace and better world, the goal, though a difficult one, could be achieved in our lifetime."

Wiesner's private researches into disarmament took him out of the country several times, and he feels that one of his most informative excursions was a visit he made to Russia in March, 1960, at the invitation of the Soviet Academy of Sciences; he was accompanied by Richard Leghorn, president of the Itek Corporation, a Massachusetts electronics firm. For three weeks, the two men travelled about the country, from Leningrad, in the north, to Tiflis, the ancient capital of Georgia, in the south. They visited a number of research institutes, and they also formed impressions of other things. Having been provided with an interpreter by the Soviet Academy, the Americans were able to converse with ordinary Soviet citizens about world politics; they repeatedly heard Russians express a deep fear and hatred of Germans. Leghorn recalls that in walking through the streets of Leningrad and pausing to chat with this passerby or that, one was sure to hear some personal account of the Nazi siege that the city had endured from 1941 to 1944—a siege of nine hundred days, in which a million people had starved to death—and that one could not stop off in Kiev without hearing of local mass murders that had been carried out by the Reichswehr. To Wiesner, this anti-German sentiment seemed so intense that he had the feeling the war was still on for most Russians. "It was an attitude, I could see, that created yet another difficulty for disarmament," he has said. "The Russians, it was clear, would never go along with any arms-control arrangement unless Germany was included."

Other journeys that Wiesner made in behalf of disarmament took him to a ski lodge at Lac Beauport, near Quebec; a resort hotel in the Austrian spa of Baden; and, in November, 1960, back to Moscow. (On this second visit to the Soviet capital, Wiesner and Walt Whitman Rostow, now head of the State Department's Policy Planning Council, successfully urged the release of two American pilots whom the Communists had jailed on the charge of espionage.) These scattered places were the settings of successive Pugwash Conferences—named for Pugwash, Nova Scotia, where the first of them was held, in 1957—in which eminent scientists from both sides of the Iron

Curtain discussed the role of science in solving problems that science had helped create. These conferences, lasting about a week each, gave the scientists a chance to think things through without the inhibiting presence of political figures. Nor were reporters present, and in the opinion of some participants this was just as well, since the proceedings were not always models of deportment. "We can get as angry and irrelevant as the next fellow," one Pugwash veteran, a Harvard scientist, has said. Wiesner found the conferences illuminating, and not only because of the papers that were presented and discussed, dealing with such topics as possible inspection systems, phases of disarmament, and coöperative international projects for exploring space. The conferences also gave him a chance to become acquainted with his colleagues from behind the Iron Curtain. Strolling with them through the Vienna Woods or sitting with them on the veranda of the ski lodge, he learned a good deal about their conceptions of history, their personalities, and their prejudices. During the conferences, they tended—as did the Westerners—to give comparatively free rein to their thoughts. Wiesner never heard any of them speak traitorously of Socialism, but their thinking, he observed, did not necessarily take a monolithic form. One wing, it was apparent, leaned toward the view that Russia must accumulate superior weapons in order to deter the West from its "war plans;" another believed that the arms race itself must be stopped while there was still time. It was essentially the same division that existed in the West, Wiesner realized, and it interested him that it should exist among Soviet scientists as well. "How does one explain this similarity?" he once asked a friend with whom he was recalling his Pugwash experiences. "Differences of opinion are standard in the West but not in Communist countries, where everybody is raised on a political philosophy that is built not on opinions but on articles of faith." One explanation, he conjectured, is that the scientists at the conferences believed they were addressing themselves to the issue of survival, rather than to that of conflicting ideologies. It was a bond that made it possible for them to reveal their fears. The Russians, it appeared, feared the spread of nuclear weapons, particularly to West Germany, and resented the fact that their country was ringed by American missile bases. And the Westerners, the Russians learned, considered the Soviet dictatorship entirely capable of springing a surprise attack. The scientists pondered the question of how these misgivings might be lessened by technical means, but it was hard for them to forget that they were nationals of rival governments. There were times when the very fears that they were seeking to overcome appeared to dominate the sessions. On one such occasion, in Baden, a renowned member of the Soviet Academy of Sciences said he was convinced that the West wanted no test-ban treaty, so he was going to leave the conference and go back to his laboratory. According to one witness—Dr. Roger Revelle, an American oceanographer who later became scientific adviser to the Secretary of the Interior—Wiesner was on his feet at once. "Jerry spoke quietly but intensely to the Russian," Revelle recalls. "He chastised him for being ready to give up on arms control. It was the most important of all the problems with which we were living, Jerry said, and we, as scientists, had a special responsibility to try to solve it. There wasn't a sound in the room for a while after Jerry sat down. We all knew we'd just heard a genuinely serious man."

❦

The views that led Wiesner to engage in arms-control activities did not include a panacea for relaxing world tensions. Rather, they amounted to a general outlook whose distinctive quality, it appears, was its element of hopefulness. Wiesner is convinced that the international situation is much too dangerous to be faced without optimism. It is an outlook he discussed one August afternoon in 1962 on a Martha's Vineyard beach with half a dozen college students, one of whom was his oldest son, Stephen, an undergraduate at the California Institute of Technology. "Without optimism, there is no generating force for new ideas," he told the young people. "Once you make up your mind that war is inevitable, there's nothing left for you to do—nothing but consider how to prepare for that war, how to win it." That sort of thinking was not likely to help matters, Wiesner went on, since it kept one from seeking for ways and means of ending the arms race. Too many people, he said, tended to look upon disarmament in either-or terms—either total disarmament or no disarmament at all—and such an approach led them to exaggerate the obstacles to arms control, which were formidable enough as it was. "One doesn't begin with perfection," Wiesner observed. As a matter of fact, he went on, he doubted whether total disarmament was attainable. "Total disarmament pretty much requires an ideal world," he said. "All I'm hoping for is a world in which police—international police—can maintain law and order." Whatever degree of disarmament was achieved, he continued, would be the culmination of a long-drawn-out process —a series of modest advances. "I call them 'low-risk steps,'" he said. "For example, suppose one country holds down the manufacture of a type of missile that another country thinks is specially tailored for its destruction. That might just make the other fellow a little less nervous, and he might then follow suit." No one he knew was in favor of unilateral disarmament, he said, and he certainly wasn't, but there were many realistic people who believed that the present array of armies and weapons could be greatly reduced without any country's really letting down its guard. "And a surprising number of those people are in the Pentagon and its counterparts abroad," he added.

Wiesner did not dwell on what might happen if the arms race got out of hand. He did say, however, that nuclear Pearl Harbors were unthinkable, because, with so many weapons already so widely dispersed, retaliation in kind was certain. But even if no country deliberately started a nuclear war, this same profusion of weapons might bring one about through an accident, or perhaps through escalation— the stepping up of a supposedly limited conflict, launched with conventional weapons. A kind of jungle suspicion was at large, he thought, and that was probably the chief obstacle to the initiation of an effective arms-control system. "How do we allay it?" he asked. "Each side reacts to threats that aren't clearly understood. Each side waits for the other to make the first conciliatory move. This is the almost ideal setting in which to lose sight of our goal of staying alive, and, of course, I don't mean as slaves. Each side has to keep trying to understand the other's real fears and real military motivations, hard though it may be. The only alternative is to repeat the old approaches, which never stopped wars in pre-nuclear times." Taking in the young faces around him, Wiesner concluded, "I don't know any more than you whether we'll ever have disarmament, but if it's going to come, I'd rather it came before another war than after."

Wiesner began making his mark as a scientist and technologist in 1929, when he was a boy of fourteen in Dearborn, Michigan. In that year, climbing half a dozen poles of a power line run by the Detroit Edison Company, he strung up a telephone wire from his own home to the home of one of his high-school classmates, a few blocks away. His private utility was eventually discontinued when his wire tangled with the power line, causing a blackout in much of Dearborn. At about the same time, he was making more socially acceptable contributions to the advancement of science by putting together various sorts of apparatus for his school's physics laboratory, an automatic scoreboard for the gymnasium, and any number of radio transmitters. He did not neglect his schoolwork for such projects, however; indeed, he was an outstanding student. "Mathematics and astronomy were my passions when I was in high school," he has said. "I can't remember a time when I wasn't thinking about science and engineering." His interests also included subjects that do not always fascinate the scientifically talented, among them literature, music, and, most notably, social issues. "It was my father who first made me curious about the way things were going in the world," he has said. "He and I would argue a lot about politics and justice and economics." Wiesner's father, a native of Austria, and his mother, a native of Hungary, had moved from Detroit, where their son was born, to Dearborn in 1918; they bought a small drygoods store there, and did moderately well, thanks to the patronage of employees at the local Ford plant. The family, which also included Wiesner's younger sister, Edna, lived in an apartment at the rear of the store and had a pleasant garden in the back yard. The boy held down an assortment of after-school jobs, one of them as a caddie at the Dearborn Country Club, a golf course that the Ford Company maintained for its top executives. Henry Ford himself often drove to the club in a Model T—he didn't play golf, but he did like to stroll around the course—and when he left, he would give Wiesner and two or three other caddies a lift home. In time, Ford became interested enough in young Wiesner to visit his high school and inspect his automatic scoreboard. The last time Ford gave Wiesner a lift was on a summer afternoon in 1934. Wiesner, who by that time had been attending the University of Michigan for a year, was walking down a dusty road when the industrialist pulled up alongside him and invited him to get in. When Ford heard that the young man was going to college, he expressed disappointment. "Mr. Ford seemed to think education was a waste of time for anyone who could do things with his hands," Wiesner has said.

Wiesner worked his way through the University of Michigan, majoring in mathematics and electrical engineering. He lived in a university-run coöperative, and in all seasons he wore a black turtleneck sweater. "Jerry has filled out a bit since those days, but at Ann Arbor his face, above that black turtleneck, was bony and gaunt, and his deep-brown eyes were soulful," a college friend who is now a physicist has recalled. "He had a St. Bernard named Thag—short for Pythagoras—who was allowed to go to classes with him, and Thag's eyes were soulful, too." Most of Wiesner's jobs at school were menial, up until his senior year, when he found one that not only paid well but introduced him to people outside his ordinary circle of math and engineering majors. This was the post of associate director in charge of technical and recording equipment at WUOM, the university's radio station. Here he met a wide variety of students and faculty members who worked for the station as writers, actors, and lecturers, and found their company exhilarating. "It didn't take me long to realize that, like my new friends, I wanted to use my particular skills, which happened to be technical, for communicating with the general public," he has said.

Wiesner received his Bachelor of Science degree in 1937 and his Master of Science degree in 1938, after which he embarked on his Ph.D. studies, while continuing his work with WUOM and also teaching an undergraduate course in broadcasting techniques. One of his students was a math major from Johnstown, Pennsylvania, named Laya Wainger—an attractive junior with a high forehead and slanting brown eyes. Everyone had a pretty good idea why she was studying broadcasting techniques. For some months, she and Wiesner had been seen strolling about the campus together, with Thag in tow, and eating together in nearby restaurants. The two were married in the summer of 1940, and Wiesner decided to interrupt his studies to take a job in Washington. (It was a long interruption, lasting until 1950, when Wiesner returned to Michigan to acquire his doctorate, and by that time his professional accomplishments were such that he may have been as well qualified as his examiners. "We didn't question Wiesner," one of them has said. "He instructed us. On every aspect of his field of research—microwave gaseous discharges—he was ready with a brilliant twenty-minute lecture.") Wiesner's post in Washington was that of chief engineer of the Library of Congress. During the next two years, in the line of duty, he accompanied Alan Lomax, the folklorist, on a tour of the South. The two men stopped off in numerous villages in Georgia, Alabama, and North Carolina that were soon to be flooded by T.V.A. dams, and interviewed scores of about-to-be-displaced persons, recording songs and recollections of the region. "Jerry came back with many beautiful recordings," Archibald MacLeish, the poet, then head of the Library, has recalled. "I remember him as a wonderfully brash young man, full of drive and outspoken about everything, which, alas, wasn't true of most Library people." Wiesner also had a hand in turning out many "Talking Books," which were records for the blind, and he developed what turned out to be a lasting interest in communications research for both the blind and the deaf. Over the years, he has collaborated with several scientists, one of them a blind physicist, on experiments aimed at feeding electronic signals through the fingertips or other parts of the skin, and at present he is chairman of the Technical Advisory Committee of the American Foundation for the Blind.

In May, 1942, Wiesner first laid eyes on the Massachusetts Institute of Technology, which has since figured prominently in his career. M.I.T. was then the headquarters of the Radiation Laboratory, where radar techniques and equipment were being developed for use against the Axis. Practically every American scientist of note put in time with the Laboratory during the war years, and Wiesner was recruited for it by Dr. Samuel A. Goudsmit, a former professor of physics at the University of Michigan, who was serving as head of the Laboratory's Theory Group. Wiesner's immediate chief was Dr. Jerrold R. Zacharias, an M.I.T. physics professor and the head of the Laboratory's Microwave Components Division. In 1944, with Zacharias's support, he was appointed Group Leader of Project Cadillac—an all-out effort to devise an airborne radar warning system that could save our warships from the suicide dives of Japanese kamikaze pilots, who had learned to come in low and avoid being detected by the radar equipment then in use. As Group Leader, Wiesner issued orders to several hundred researchers, scattered all over the country; Project Cadillac commanded priorities as high as those of our nuclear-bomb effort, and it succeeded in designing radar equipment that could spot the kamikazes. "Jerry was then only twenty-eight," Zacharias has recalled, "but he impressed me as one of the best electrical engineers I'd ever seen, and he seemed positively eager for responsibility, which is important for an engineer. Unlike a physicist, an engineer can't wait for genius to strike. He has to deliver his work on time, or *x* number of people will be standing around unemployed." Wiesner's work wasn't all indoors. During his years with the Laboratory, he often worked side by side with servicemen testing electronic equipment, and went on flights to test the equipment further. More than once, he was on hand at Quonset Point Naval Air Base, in Rhode Island, in the dark hours of early morning, to put the finishing touches on the radar equipment of fighters bound for the Pacific. Later on, he did the same thing at the Presque Isle Air Force Base, in Maine, for B-17s taking off for Britain with different radar apparatus. In recognition of his work, he was awarded the Certificate of Merit by President Truman.

After the war ended, Wiesner and his wife spent a year in Los Alamos, New Mexico, where he helped plan the electronic instrumentation for the Bikini bomb tests. The Wiesners' first child, Stephen, had been born in Cambridge, and their second, Zachary (after Dr. Zacharias), was born in Los Alamos. Since then, they have had two more children—Lisa and Joshua. In the fall of 1946, Wiesner took a job on the M.I.T. faculty as a professor of communications engineering. It was a perfect move, he says, for he was introduced to remarkable equipment and worked with remarkable colleagues, all of them eager to put to use the wartime advances that had been made in the field of communications. "Communications," of course, covers a wide variety of activities, but at M.I.T., and other scientific centers, it includes the branch of knowledge that has come into being with the development of electrical communication and control systems and computers; as the study of communications, in this sense, has become refined, it had led to new understandings in many other fields, all broadly within the domain of epistemology, or the study of knowledge itself. One of Wiesner's colleagues was the mathematician Dr. Norbert Wiener, who pioneered the new field and gave it the name of cybernetics. In Wiesner's early days at M.I.T., Wiener organized a series of supper seminars dealing with the wider implications of cybernetics, which were held in a restaurant near the campus, and were attended by mathematicians, physicists, electrical engineers, philologists, psychologists, biologists, and neurosurgeons, all of whom hoped that the discussions might lead to fresh insights into their own disciplines. It was a hope based on the resemblance between electrical signals and the signals transmitted by our nerve fibres—on the fact that electrical systems and nervous systems often appear to handle signals in the same way—and it was a hope that, to a surprising degree, has been realized over the years. The seminars, which Wiesner regards as one of the intellectual high points of his life, confirmed a conviction he had long held—that the various types of communications have much in common. "Communication is dependent on symbols, for messages can be transmitted only by means of symbols that have an agreed-upon meaning, and this applies whether the messages are being transmitted between two devices, two human beings, or two cultures," Wiesner has said. "If the symbols don't mean the same thing to the sender and the receiver, communication is blurred. Take the word 'rain,' for instance. It has one set of connotations for a Berber in the Sahara and another set for an Indian in the monsoon country. Linguists, you know, speak of such confusions as 'semantic noise,' and 'noise' is also the term that engineers use to describe random electrical signals that blur messages."

Wiesner himself has done considerable research on the second sort of noise, and has written several papers on it. Another paper, which he wrote in collaboration with Dr. Y. W. Lee, a professor of electrical engineering at M.I.T., is concerned with such matters as improving techniques for radar sensitivity—techniques that have enabled scientists at M.I.T. to make radar contact with Venus. Still another has to do with the scatter propagation of radio waves, which enables us to send and receive signals, or "see," beyond the horizon; its findings have had far-reaching military applications, particularly in the setting up of warning systems against surprise attacks. Wiesner has written other papers, too, but his scholarly output is meagre compared to his production of government reports. "As a scientist, Jerry has to pay a price for his social-mindedness," one M.I.T. colleague has said. Nevertheless, Wiesner's professional accomplishments are of sufficiently high calibre to have won him admission to the National Academy of Sciences, in 1960—a distinction that is shared by very few engineers. "Jerry is definitely one of the men who have raised electronics from a fairly primitive pursuit to one with philosophical value," says I. I. Rabi, a Nobel Prize winner in physics who was associate director of the Radiation Laboratory from 1940 to 1945. Discussing Wiesner's place in the communications movement, another physicist, an M.I.T. professor, has said, "Perhaps one might put it that Wiener preached the gospel and Wiesner organized the church. Jerry's real strength, I think, lies in his ability to spot the potential importance of an idea long before others do. He wants to assist in the realization of the new physics. I don't know that I would call his a creative mind—he isn't likely to supply the things that are missing. But give him a chance at the components that are present, and you can bet on him to put them in place, so keen is his organizing intelligence."

Whatever Wiesner's position in the hierarchy of the communications movement may be, he became director of the M.I.T. Research Laboratory of Electronics in 1952, and in 1959 was given the additional post of chairman of the school's Department of Electrical Engineering. The Laboratory is one of the world's great communications-research centers, with a staff of five hundred and fifty and with an astonishing array of computers that—given the proper "programming," or instructions—are capable of doing such things as proving geometric theorems, translating Russian into understandable, if unidiomatic, English, and pairing off to play chess. As part of M.I.T.'s centennial celebration, one of these machines "wrote" a television Western about a robber and a sheriff, with appropriate gunplay, that was put on in the course of a C.B.S. television program called "The Thinking Machine," in October, 1960. Wiesner was on hand to explain to the actor David Wayne, appearing as the average man, how the computer-author operated. "We forgot to instruct the machine to put in a heroine," Wiesner has recalled. Shortly after he became the White House science adviser, the same machine set him a letter. "Dear Jerry, I miss you," it went. "I hope you are enjoying your job in Washington." As head of the Laboratory, Wiesner found it highly stimulating to watch the machines perform tasks set by, for example, a neurosurgeon, an art historian, a sociologist, or a philologist. "Jerry is excellent at what the computer people call code-switching," Dr. Roman Jakobson, one of the world's renowned philologists, who teaches at both M.I.T. and Harvard, once said. "I do not know what the cost is to him of being a constructive busybody, but he is able to juggle ten different matters without neglecting any of the important aspects of any of them." While running the Laboratory, Wiesner found time to join other faculty members in a successful drive to create new courses in history, literature, and economics and to find scholars of stature to teach them. "Wiesner has had a pervasive influence here," says Dr. James R. Killian, the chairman of M.I.T.'s board of trustees, who was also one of Wiesner's two predecessors in the post of White House scientific adviser. "He is not so much a day-by-day manager as an innovator—a remarkably fine one, always throwing up ideas, doing something about them with enormous energy, and, it goes without saying, using his gifts as a first-rate engineer-scientist."

As an administrator, Wiesner did not exactly run a taut ship; the Laboratory had no tidy table of organization and no titles, and there was little severity about enforcing budgets and little hesitation in delegating authority. He did, however, have his own way of instilling a strong feeling of cohesion and discipline. "Once Jerry was back of you, there was nothing halfway about it, and that spurred you on," Professor Walter Rosenblith, an M.I.T. biophysicist whose special field is the communications processes of the brain, has said. "I believe it's his sense of commitment—or perhaps backbone is what I mean—that gives him his extra drive, and that drive certainly explains, in part, why he's come to be the President's scientific adviser."

In those years, Wiesner's sense of commitment spread beyond M.I.T. One afternoon in September, 1959, while he was alone in his home, in Watertown,

Massachusetts, just outside Cambridge, nursing a case of the flu, a deputation of neighbors came to the door; they were looking for Mrs. Wiesner.

"We'd like her to run for the Watertown Planning Board on the Democratic ticket," a spokesman informed the scientist.

"She's not home," Wiesner said. "How about my running?"

"That would be wonderful, Professor Wiesner," the spokesman said, and the group departed.

As soon as Wiesner was back on his feet, he began campaigning, and on Election Day he won a decisive victory. He was still grappling with Watertown's traffic and zoning problems when President-elect Kennedy called him to Washington.

Wiesner's sense of commitment had been demonstrated in a different way in 1953, when he found himself up against McCarthyism. His difficulties arose out of a charge of "sabotage" that had been made against the "Voice of America" staff by one of its employees and that was being investigated by the Senate Permanent Invesigating Subcommittee. The charge hinged on whether the State Department had chosen the proper sites for two transmitters that would send "Voice" radio programs abroad. The Radio Corporation of America and the Army Signal Corps, after making surveys, had already agreed that the sites were proper when a representative of Senator McCarthy came to M.I.T. to ask Wiesner to declare publicly that the Department's choice amounted to sabotage. "I refused, and the man turned nasty," Wiesner recounts. The next thing he knew, a friend of his in Washington informed him that his security clearance, which was vital to his work, was in jeopardy. Wiesner never did lose his clearance, but the possibility shook him. "I decided to make money," he says. "I wanted to be financially independent, so that no matter what happened, I could always express my opinions. There may have been a variety of reasons back of my decision, but the McCarthy business was certainly one of them." In 1955, with Zacharias, Rabi, and several other physicist and engineers, Wiesner founded Hycon Electric, Inc., a firm that specialized in developing and marketing various types of electronic equipment and in taking on research jobs for the government. In due course, Wiesner became the chairman of the board, and the firm changed its name to the Hermes Electronic Company. In the late nineteen-fifties, too, working on a retainer basis, he served as a consultant to several other companies. His earnings from these ventures into the business world have enabled him to do various things he might otherwise never have contemplated. For instance, in recent years he has bought a summer home and a tract of land on Martha's Vineyard, has contributed rather sizable sums to independent radio and television stations around the country, and has come to the assistance of less affluent friends and colleagues; according to Professor Max F. Millikan, director of M.I.T.'s Center for International Studies, he helped buy a special type of computer for a student—a man of forty with a family—who needed it in preparing his doctoral thesis. Indeed, his earnings probably enabled him to afford to accept his present position, which pays twenty-two thousand five hundred dollars a year—less than half of what he earned as an M.I.T. professor, corporation executive, and industrial consultant.

Busy as Wiesner was during the fifties, he found time to carry out a number of government assignments, including service on President Eisenhower's Science Advisory Committee. He was summoned to Washington so frequently that sometimes for months at a stretch he could devote no more than fifteen minutes every two weeks to each of a number of graduate students whom he was advising on their research. "It's a tribute to Jerry that the students remained with him," a colleague has said. Nor was Washington the only place he visited; he went, it seemed, wherever armament or disarmament was being discussed. Sometimes he gave his attention to military research, and at other times, acting either in behalf of our government or as a private citizen, he attended conferences aimed at arresting the arms race. To all these pursuits, he brought his customary indefatigability—a trait that made him a key figure in conferences rather than just another participant. A Harvard physicist who has served on many committees with Wiesner has said, "Committee decisions usually end up being made by a couple of fellows who are willing to stay on and work like dogs after everybody else has gone home. Well, Jerry was always one of those fellows."

Wiesner was as busy with extracurricular activities at home as he was abroad. M.I.T. itself was the scene of many weapons studies in which he had a hand, and as for the exploring of arms-control ideas, there was no end of that in Cambridge. Many distinguished men in and around Cambridge were concerned about the arms race, among them McGeorge Bundy, who was then Dean of Harvard's Faculty of Arts and Sciences and later became the President's Special Assistant for National Security Affairs; Carl Kaysen, a Harvard professor of economics who became Bundy's right-hand man in Washington; Walt Whitman Rostow, a professor of economic history at M.I.T. who became chairman of the State Department's Policy Planning Council; Arthur Schlesinger, Jr., the Harvard historian, who later served as a special assistant to the President; J. Kenneth Galbraith, the Harvard economist, who was appointed Ambassador to India; Edward M. Purcell, a Harvard professor and a Nobel laureate in physics; Edwin H. Land, the physicist who invented the Polaroid camera; and Wiesner's friend Zacharias. So often did Wiesner and thirty-five or forty associates weigh the complexities of arms control and other military and political issues—usually in a free university classroom or at someone's home—that, in spirit at least, they eventually constituted a kind of informal club. Numerous articles, broadcasts, and letters to newspapers on the subject of arms control resulted from this Cambridge ferment, but up until the winter of 1960 the informal club carried no political weight. That changed, however, when it acquired an ex-officio member in the person of Senator John F.

Kennedy. Often, upon returning to Boston from Washington, the Senator would draw on the supply of brain power so conveniently at hand on the west bank of the Charles. Right at the start, Wiesner was put forward as a man who could supply the Senator with expert knowledge of our defenses and of approaches to arms control—issues that were bound to arise in the coming campaign for the Presidency—and the Senator learned through inquiries he made in Cambridge, Washington, and elsewhere that Wiesner was in fact probably as well informed on these matters as anyone in the country. Moreover, as the Senator also learned, Wiesner's reputation among scientists everywhere could hardly have been higher. "By the time Kennedy came into his life, Jerry was one of a certain élite who could be bought not by money but only by a national problem," Herbert G. Weiss, an electrical engineer who is associated with the Lincoln Laboratory at M.I.T., once told a friend.

As the year went on, Senator Kennedy saw more and more of Wiesner during his visits to Boston. The association continued throughout the campaign, in which Wiesner worked closely with writers who were preparing speeches on disarmament, defense, and related issues. After the Democratic victory, there was little suspense among scientists as to whom the President-elect was likely to choose as his Special Assistant for Science and Technology. Early in January, at a gathering in Schlesinger's home, the President-elect, momentarily finding himself alone with Wiesner, invited him to join the new administration.

❦

Wiesner's working quarters in Washington are in the Old State Department Building, an ornate five-story structure, some twenty yards from the West Wing of the White House, that now serves as a part of the President's Executive Offices. The Special Assistant for Science and Technology and his aides occupy a corner of the second floor, sharing the building with the staffs of the President's Special Assistant for National Security Affairs, the President's Council of Economic Advisers, the Director of the Budget, and other executive agencies. Wiesner has twenty-eight people working for him, a small staff, considering that, directly or indirectly, what goes on in his office may influence the government's annual expenditure of fourteen billion dollars for research-and-development undertakings. However, Wiesner may call upon a wide variety of organizations for assistance, including the President's Science Advisory Committee, which is composed of distinguished consultants, and whose panels concern themselves with all branches of science; the Federal Council for Science and Technology, which is made up of the chairman of the Atomic Energy Commission, the Defense Department's Director of Research and Engineering, and other ranking officials responsible for scientific matters inside the government, and which deliberates on such matters as recruiting trained manpower, smoothing out inter-agency difficulties, and shaping policy on research grants to universities; the National Science Foundation, which makes grants for basic research; and the National Academy of Sciences, which conducts long-range studies on behalf of the government.

Wiesner hopes that his staff will retain its present compactness. He has no dreams of leading a phalanx of thousands, for bigness, he believes, would undermine the value of his office, which, as he points out, is consultative rather than executive. "It's that consultant function of ours that frees us from bureaucratic encrustation," he says. "We deal in ideas and problems, not in power plays." As Wiesner sees it, his assignment is to try to give the President the proper perspective on scientific issues and to relate technical questions to policy considerations in such a way that Mr. Kennedy may pass on their merits. To be sure, Wiesner adds, he may be deputized to handle particular jobs on his own, but his primary task is to sort out and assess conflicting opinions, summarizing their pros and cons for the President. His view of the scientific scene, he says, must always be a broad one; above all, it must be free from "mission bias"—a Washington phrase for the average agency's narrow, and perhaps justifiable, instinct to further its own interests, if only through simple aggrandizement. Wiesner's approach is certainly in keeping with the original conception of the job, according to Killian, the first of the three men who have thus far held it. "When President Eisenhower asked me to come down from M.I.T., in November, 1957, he told me that he wanted someone to help him who wasn't involved in internal administration warfare," Killian has recalled. "The President wanted a consulting engineer, so to speak, with whom he could count on maintaining a confidential relationship." Besides being a "consulting engineer," according to David Z. Beckler, a federal official of long standing who is now one of Wiesner's aides, the adviser should be a science reporter for the President. "The adviser is the man who stands on deck and watches for icebergs," Beckler has said, adding that the need for an adviser became startlingly clear on October 4, 1957, with the launching of the Soviet Union's first Sputnik. The President, a flabbergasted layman casting about for an explanation, discovered that there wasn't really anyone he could turn to— that his administration included no one scientist in a position to keep him posted, responsibly and consistently, on scientific developments. "The way things stood, the President couldn't have justifiably bawled out anyone, even if he'd wanted to," Beckler has observed.

Consultative or not, Wiesner's role is by no means a passive one. Figuratively speaking—and sometimes literally, too—he may wander all over the federal establishment in the course of one of his arduous days, which last well into the evening. Wiesner generally arrives at the Old State Department Building at eight-thirty in the morning, after a twenty-minute trip in a chauffeur-driven government car from his home in Chevy Chase. At that hour, he rarely knows what the day holds in store, partly because the President may want him at any moment and partly because he consistently tends to overload his calendar. "He always thinks there's room on it for just one more appointment," his secretary, Miss Irene Benik, once remarked. Still, he is fairly sure that he will have to cope with a few emergencies before the day is over. A report may suddenly come in to the effect that an important phase of our overseas technical-aid program is in danger of being bungled, in which case Secretary of State Rusk may want to get together with Wiesner. There may be a fresh public outcry about fallout, prompting Wiesner to ask the Federal Radiation Council to try once again to evaluate conflicting expert views on "permissible" levels of exposure. If there has just been a rash of near collisions between military and commercial planes, there may be a meeting in Wiesner's office attended by representatives of the Federal Aviation Agency and the Defense Department. His day will almost certainly include a number of not-so-urgent matters as well. When the President decorated the seven astronauts, Wiesner and Mrs. Kennedy were delegated to chat with them for an hour. Every now and then, Wiesner is called on to do some decorating himself; on occasion for instance, he has presented medals to the young winners of a science competition. Groups of high-school science teachers visiting Washington are likely to call on him and ask him for a few words on the state of American science and technology. High foreign dignitaries are likely to do the same, and Wiesner, naturally, must appear at his most leisurely during their usually leisurely visits. And there is always correspondence to handle—

exasperating piles of it, Wiesner says, though now and then a piece of mail comes through that presents a pleasant problem. For example, shortly after assuming his present post, he was touched, and made a trifle nostalgic, when the revered M.I.T. mathematician Norbert Wiener wrote him that the proprietress of a Chinese restaurant near the school was afraid her cuisine would fall off unless the State Department let her have a decent chef from Formosa. The mathematician said he hoped that "notwithstanding the heavy labors you have and the work of life and death which you are engaged in . . . you can find it possible to drop a hint at the right place."

Wiesner is often to be seen, coatless, in his outer office, striding about restlessly as he dictates a letter to Miss Benik or her assistant, and occasionally picking up a phone or permitting himself the solace of a sour ball—one of a supply that he keeps in an old-fashioned glass candy jar for waiting visitors. His own office is a comfortable, spacious, high-ceilinged room with a fine view of the White House lawn; it easily accommodates not only Wiesner's large desk, a Barca Lounger, and a movable blackboard but a long conference table with places for ten. The walls are adorned with framed color photographs of rural New England scenes and a photograph of the President, inscribed, "To Jerry, who makes the complex simple."

The sight of the inscription may remind Wiesner of an intricate, highly expensive apparatus for nuclear research that he wants to discuss with the President—a type of linear accelerator, or atom smasher, that may cost the government more than a hundred million dollars. Wiesner has described the equipment in memorandums to the President, but he intends to discuss it with him further. Being a notoriously impulsive phoner, he is tempted to dial Mr. Kennedy. He holds off, though, because he is reluctant to take up Mr. Kennedy's time. However, the President, who is quite a phoner himself, rings his adviser a little later. He has read the memorandums, the President says, and he has a few questions. Is Wiesner free? Dropping everything, Wiesner takes the familiar walk to the White House, his brain spinning with possible ways of further simplifying the complex for his distinguished student. The two men, bent over a scratch pad in a small library in the White House living quarters, make rapid headway with the accelerator. As it happens, Wiesner has said, the President is an easy man to tutor. "It's a break for me that he is," Wiesner continued. "The fact is that he goes straight to the heart of an issue. I'm not suggesting that he knows how to design a microwave antenna, but he can judge the comparative merits of different models, once things have been explained to him. And he doesn't make the sometimes fuzzy assumptions that a scientist might, so his questions often have a fresh, penetrating quality. When he first took office, I was one of a few men who had to brief him, over a period of weeks, on the technical facts of American military power. It was a concentrated dose of some pretty grim details that even Senators don't get to know, and throughout it all his questions remained cool and direct."

After leaving the President, Wiesner may reflect that his explanation of the accelerator was not precisely the academic matter it might have been at a university. Without mentioning it—without needing to—the President and his adviser were aware that they were discussing the atom smasher against a background made up of such factors as the state of research in rival nations and the budgetary competition that the accelerator might meet with from other American projects. No topic of discussion in the White House is ever academic, Wiesner has said, regardless of how purely technical it may appear to be. He has come to realize that the President of the United States is duty bound to reduce everything to political reality as he sees it. "The President must fit everything into the world picture," Wiesner once told a friend. "This is especially true when it comes to science, and not only because the effort may result in such prizes as superior weapons and propaganda coups. The President fully understands that there is another incentive, beyond these. He knows that the country whose science is limber and alert and ingenious and imaginative is sure to count as a political force." As an example of the indivisibility of science and the "world picture," Wiesner cites the problems surrounding aphthous fever, or hoof-and-mouth disease. The fever is a subject seemingly quite remote from international politics, yet for the better part of a year his office has been looking into a claim by the government of Argentina, where the disease is widespread among cattle, that its processed beef is safe for export to the American market. Obviously, this question has economic implications for Argentina that could strongly affect her political attitude toward us, and at present the entire affair is in the hands of experts, American and Argentine, who are trying, by means of vaccines and improved food processing, to bring about a happy ending. When the subject of experts comes up, Wiesner is sometimes impelled to make a few general remarks about them. "An expert is only a relative idea," he says, and goes on to explain that when he first described the nature of hoof-and-mouth disease to the President, Mr. Kennedy was quite aware that his adviser had himself been advised by a dozen virologists, biologists, entomologists, and food processors before coming to the White House. "The chain of *expertise* in science is unending," Wiesner says, "but, unfortunately, many people tend to regard experts as omniscient. This is a mistaken humility. Scientists don't want the public to be overawed by their technical jargon. Such a public attitude puts them in the position of being accountable not only for the scientific aspects of their work but for its social effects, too, which is not fair. If there's to be an expert on those effects, it should be the public itself."

Wiesner's talks at the White House often deal with what he calls "sleepless problems"—critical situations on which action must be taken before adequate information is available. Matters bearing on war and peace often fall into this category—test-ban and disarmament negotiations, for instance, and the deployment of our military resources. Wiesner is sometimes appalled by the speed with which the knottiest issue may have to be resolved; the kind of thinking he must do is a far cry from the quiet reflection that is possible at a university. "University scientists are seldom given a problem that has to be solved within a day or two," he says. "Down here, though, situations boil up fast, and you have to form your judgments equally fast. For instance, it would take a year to fully test and evaluate the unmanned automatic seismic stations that the Soviet Union has proposed as a device for eliminating the necessity for on-site inspection in policing a nuclear-test ban. But we can't let a year pass by without responding to a proposal of that kind, so we have to make a rapid assessment based on the information we have, and pass it on to our test-ban delegates in Geneva. Then, as we continue to study the matter, we can only hope the assessment will stand up. Of course, that same haste sometimes tends to make us too cautious—too repetitious—in our assessments."

Wiesner, of course, is not the only man with whom the President talks over "sleepless problems." Many other advisers, military and civilian, have their say about them before the President makes up his mind, and this is very much to Wiesner's liking, since he recognizes the fact that the problems are much too heavily charged with political elements to be settled solely on the basis of scientific considerations. The dilemmas that come before the President, he has said, cannot be made artificially simple, like controlled experiments in a laboratory. How, for instance, could the scientific method have been applied in our decision in April, 1962, to resume atmospheric testing of nuclear weapons? On the one hand, aerial shots would be far cheaper and more informative than underground shots; on the other hand, such tests might not be so cheap in terms of political reaction around the world. With its jumble of technical and political aspects, the problem could be decided only by what Wiesner calls "a flash of intuition." "Even if the wisest Nobel laureate in physics were President, he would have to fall back on intuition," Wiesner has said. "Some problems are just too complicated for rational, logical solutions. They admit of insights, not answers." Wiesner, naturally, has his own political reactions, the same as anyone else, scientist or layman, but he does his best to present technical details objectively, and at least one military man who has attended White House talks with him is impressed with his efforts. "Time and again, I've heard Wiesner put technical stuff so lucidly and—well—so neutrally that I was sure he was risking the defeat of his own convictions," this officer has told an acquaintance. Early in the Kennedy Administration, Wiesner arranged for the President to discuss a possible nuclear-test ban with Dr. Edward Teller, "the father of the H-bomb." Teller's and Wiesner's conceptions of the arms race are almost diametrically opposed.

Back at his desk after his visit to the White House, Wiesner, glancing at his calendar, may note that a member of the Cabinet will be calling on him after lunch. Wiesner hopes that every Secretary who has not done so already will appoint an Assistant Secretary who could act as an adviser on science and technology—who would do for the Secretary, that is, what Wiesner does for the President. It is a dream of Wiesner's to see a science adviser in practically every federal agency, and of late he has been urging the scheme on Secretary of Agriculture Orville Freeman, arguing that such an Assistant Secretary would have plenty of work, for he would need to tie together such concerns of the department as improving strains of plants and animals, devising new ways of coping with plant diseases, and perfecting techniques of refrigeration. The new Assistant Secretaries might not do away with mission bias, Wiesner concedes, but they would spread scientific intelligence and perspective throughout the government. So far, two members of the Cabinet have accepted the idea—the Secretary of the Interior and the Secretary of Commerce. Both men are delighted with the way things have worked out. Interior Secretary Stewart Udall's adviser, whom he appointed on Wiesner's recommendation, is Dr. Roger Revelle, of the Scripps Institute of Oceanography. "Revelle has been of immense help to me, and I have Jerry to thank," Udall has told a friend. "Jerry talked to me, with his usual depth and acuity, about science as an instrument of government. He pointed out that the field of natural resources, which is the responsibility of my department, is becoming increasingly complex, and then he explained how a scientific adviser could help me keep up with what's going on and also help me coördinate the work itself."

In the summer of 1961, when Mohammed Ayub Khan, the President of Pakistan, came to Washington on a state visit, Udall had particular reason to be grateful for Revelle's presence on his staff. President Ayub used the occasion to inform President Kennedy that water was drowning Pakistan's crops, ruining a hundred thousand acres yearly. Pakistan, it appeared, lay atop the world's largest underground reservoir; the water had risen close to the surface, absorbing salts as it did so, and consequently had prevented plants from growing, and even made the land barren. Mr. Kennedy told the Asian leader that he would have his scientific adviser look into the matter, and Wiesner, in turn, sought Revelle's advice. "I'm lucky that we have Roger in Interior—a man who not only knows water but has a broad outlook," Wiesner said at the time. Subsequently, he and Revelle made a field trip to Pakistan, where, protected from the sun by pith helmets, they travelled by jeep through much of the Punjab. The two men, with the assistance of a host of hydrologists, agronomists, chemists, economists, and other experts, came to the conclusion that they could turn the underground water into an asset by pumping it to the surface and using it for irrigation. Even more important, the group saw that Pakistan's agriculture was far too primitive, and Revelle has recommended a balanced program that he believes will eventually triple the country's crop yields. Farmers are being exposed to Western methods; they are being taught to plant seeds in rows instead of sowing them broadcast, and to use fertilizers and pesticides. "If all goes well," Wiesner has said, "Pakistan, which has the world's fifth-largest population, may be a modern country by 1980."

Wiesner thinks that our foreign aid in general can benefit from the sort of technical analysis that has been carried out in Pakistan. "At first, we not only made plenty of mistakes in our overseas operations but failed to recognize the successes we had," he once told a friend. The relation between foreign aid, political and social progress, and science is a delicate and almost indefinable one, in his opinion, but he has said, "If there is any connection between a society's physical condition and the political conditions that its people are willing to tolerate—and I think there is—then scientific intelligence does have an impact on the political outcome." The statement, though cautious, reflects Wiesner's basic optimism. Research of all kinds, he believes, can make our overseas operations more efficient. Anthropology, for instance, has turned up useful data, according to Eugene B. Skolnikoff, a member of Wiesner's staff who, among other things, watches for snags in our foreign-aid program. We now know enough not to ship jeeps just anywhere; natives of some remote lands consider them "dead" when their sparkplugs give out, and thereupon push them off the road and abandon them. We have also learned that certain tribesmen are less than grateful when we send them food-processing equipment that requires the use of hot water; to these people hot water is taboo, for they believe that it harms the spirits of their ancestors.

Before the morning is over, Wiesner will very likely go back to the outer office, help himself to a sour ball, drop onto a leather sofa, and start dictating. An assistant may poke his head in to ask a question—perhaps Michael Michaelis, who serves as Wiesner's liaison with the Civilian Technology Panel, a group of assorted experts that works closely with the Commerce Department and the President's Council of Economic Advisers on matters having to do with the reinvigoration of American industry. Michaelis may ask Wiesner if he will have time later in the day to meet a visiting businessman. Despite a disapproving glance from Miss Benik, Wiesner will probably agree. On one such occasion, Michaelis brought in Robert E. Simon, Jr., a man who has been planning to build a satellite city outside Washington, near the Dulles International Airport. Satellite cities interest Wiesner, because he considers them an integral part of our future civilian technology, and he is by no means satisfied with how far our present technology has brought us. "In relation to its potentialities," Wiesner has said, "the United States is as underdeveloped a country as Nigeria."

Wiesner undoubtedly had many things in mind when he said this, for he has long been preoccupied with ways of keeping the American plant from running down too badly. Our economy, he has noted, had better be in shape by the turn of the next century, for our population will have doubled by then and its needs will be immense. He believes that thirty or forty years from now the congestion may be such that many commuters to Washington will live in satellite cities somewhere in West Virginia. Wiesner envisions these commuters as coming to work aboard a jet-propelled train that travels at three hundred miles an hour. Trains, he predicts, are going to figure prominently in our lives within a few decades, and so are other forms of public ground transportation, for soon all planes will be travelling at supersonic speeds, which means that the distances between airports will have to be great. He deplores the moribund state of today's railroads, and he has assigned Michaelis the task of rounding up ideas for their improvement. Wiesner thinks that our rail lines are operating on the basis of a technology that was mainly developed about fifty years ago, but then, he says, so are some of our other industries—textiles, for instance, and, to a lesser extent, housing. If industries like these are to be resuscitated, Wiesner says, they will need ideas that are both practical and radical. The right people and the right agencies have to be jogged into thinking up such ideas and putting them into effect, and his office is trying its best to bring these people and agencies together. The Civilian Technology Panel has been given the responsibility for effecting this, and it has the President's full blessing; in fact, Wiesner says, the panel owes its existence to Mr. Kennedy's concern about potential soft spots in our economy. "The President feels that our economy is in a position to be stimulated by innovation, and the industries where innovation is the rule—electronics and communications—seem to bear out his idea," Wiesner observes. "They're in a flourishing state, while our backward industries are showing neither a proper rate of growth nor a proper profit."

Returning to his desk, Wiesner may concern

himself with the activities of another panel—a panel, headed by his old friend Zacharias, whose work could bring about an improvement in our civilian technology as well as in certain other fields. This is the Panel on Educational Research and Development, whose objective is to raise teaching standards in all subjects—scientific and non-scientific—from elementary school on up, and which has been at work since February, 1961, in conjunction with the Office of Education and the National Science Foundation. Wiesner hopes particularly that the panel may help America turn out more and better technicians—an accomplishment that, in his opinion, depends in large measure on the ability of scientists to persuade the public that the ways of science are not so mysterious. In an address before the annual dinner of the Weizmann Institute in New York in December, 1961, he said, "Because I have a deep conviction that the practice of a science or of engineering in the proper social setting can be one of the most satisfying activities that man has ever devised for himself, I have a certain confidence that a widespread acquaintance with science and technology will of itself bring into being all the professional practitioners that we could possibly use, and perhaps a few more than that."

Such a "widespread acquaintance," according to Wiesner, is being stymied by inadequate teaching methods, and it is to the question of how to go about eliminating this inadequacy that Zacharias's panel is addressing its efforts. Certainly, Wiesner says, moving pictures, recordings, teaching machines, and experimental models can be put to wider and, at the same time, more judicious use in the dissemination of scientific knowledge than they are being put to now. It is odd, he thinks, that our university scientists and engineers, whose techniques have proved so effective in the laboratory, haven't really got around to making an applied science of teaching itself—the very activity for which they draw their pay. Wiesner would also like to see a keener interest in the so-called life sciences—biology, psychology, anthropology, and others—which haven't come in for the same degree of attention as physics. And he finds it dismaying to contemplate the great number of people who now pass their days in ignorance of the forces that are shaping their lives. "That's an awful plight, it seems to me," he says. "I imagine such people feel bewildered and put upon. It must be especially hard for them to have a satisfying, confident view of themselves or the world, and that's one thing all of us can use right now."

❦

Unless something unforeseen arises, Wiesner will quite possibly be lunching at the Pentagon. More than half of his working time is taken up with matters relating to the Defense Department, and this is only natural, since more than half of the government's funds for research and development are spent by that agency. Wiesner has driven to the Pentagon hundreds of times in his government car but he has not yet come to think of these trips as routine. Whenever his car approaches the Pentagon, he is still conscious that he is about to set foot in one of the world's important buildings—one of those repositories of force to be found in every capital. Force, as Wiesner conceives of it, pervades everything, like air, and, perhaps more precisely than most people, he knows how it can be used for good or ill. The thought of its duality is likely to occur to him anew whenever he wanders the Pentagon's bays and rings to meet with our high-ranking military leaders.

Wiesner has regular luncheon appointments with two sets of Pentagon officials. Once a month, in the private dining room of Secretary of Defense Robert McNamara, he meets with a group that includes the Secretary, Deputy Secretary Roswell L. Gilpatric, and Dr. Harold Brown, the Defense Department's Director of Defense Research and Engineering. Once a week, he and one of his assistants, Spurgeon Keeny, meet with Brown and the Assistant Secretaries for Research and Development for the three services: James H. Wakelin, Jr., of the Navy; Finn J. Larsen, of the Army; and Brockway McMillan, of the Air Force. The atmosphere at these sessions is almost always cordial, even though Wiesner is the President's man, and is thus, in McNamara's words, thrust into the role of "an institutionalized gadfly." (The Secretary ritualistically opens each meeting by inquiring, "And now what are we doing wrong?") "Jerry never stops asking tough-minded, penetrating questions," McNamara has told a friend. "His mind ranges far beyond the interests of the average scientist." Nevertheless, Wiesner tries to keep from being overinquisitive about the way things are actually run. "It must be frustrating for him now and then, because he knows so much about military problems himself," Brown has said. "I think he's operating most effectively in a difficult setup." The questions that Wiesner does ask are aimed at gathering information worth the President's attention. For instance, if our military establishment is thinking of replacing one kind of weapon with another, Mr. Kennedy might feel that such a step would convey an excessively bellicose impression to other governments. Or if the men in the dining rooms are comparing the merits of missiles and aircraft in particular situations, or trying to devise a space policy that would eliminate some of the rivalry between the Defense Department and the National Aeronautics and Space Administration, the President will also have to be consulted on that matter. Ten years ago, Wiesner was alarmed by the backwardness of our military technology. Today, he also watches out for signs that the pendulum may have swung the other way. Are plans now afoot, for example, to land battalions on the moon? They are not, but the President's adviser must be alert for glamorous projects of this sort, which may be a little too glamorous for our practical good.

The conferees often bring up the subject of disarmament, which, Wiesner says, is not a fighting word in the Pentagon, as most people suspect. Nor is it true, he adds, that soldiers would necessarily be thrown out of work if disarmament ever arrived. Their discipline and their knowledge of weapons would make them exceptionally well-qualified sentinels of an arms-control treaty. In 1961, Wiesner has remarked, Secretary McNamara appointed eleven officers, headed by an admiral, to staff the Weapons Evaluation and Control Bureau of the government's new Arms Control and Disarmament Agency, and at the height of the Cuban crisis a detachment of U.N. military men stood ready to oversee the dismantling of the Soviet rocket bases. There is nothing phony about the interest that his military associates at both luncheon groups take in disarmament, Wiesner maintains; like practically all other government officials he has observed since going to Washington, they seem to feel that arms control is where greatness lies. Along with everybody else, they realize that an end to the arms race could end the present insecurity, but, as Wiesner often points out, it takes a certain determination to remember this in the midst of the suspicion engendered daily by international moves and countermoves. Wiesner admits that his own determination isn't always as sturdy as it might be. Sometimes even he, optimist that he is, finds himself wondering if the die may not have already been cast without our realizing it—if we aren't just hanging around waiting for the details to unfold. Such moods don't last long, however. "I know that disarmament won't come easily," he says. "It will take sweeping political action—as sweeping, in its way, as a declaration of war. It can't possibly be achieved without a struggle, but I think almost everybody knows it's a struggle worth going on with."

5
The Peaceable Gypsies

As Dr. Wiesner himself had frequently mentioned to me, he was hardly unique among his colleagues in discussing the social effects of his work, for now, in contrast to those days long ago, before there were nuclear weapons, science is not all that scientists talk about when they get together. Nowadays they also talk politics—the momentous, dilemma-ridden politics that are largely a by-product of their own experiments. Indeed, they sometimes travel great distances to do so—the most notable example of this being the attendance of scientists from all over the world at the so-called Pugwash Conferences, more formally known as the International Conferences on Science and World Affairs. While Pugwash, Nova Scotia, was the site of the first conference, in July, 1957, about a dozen subsequent ones have been held, at irregular intervals, in such widely scattered parts of the globe as Russia, the United States, Austria, and England, and while the participants have included historians, law professors, and other such scholars, the meetings have primarily involved physicists, biologists, and chemists, many of them Nobel Prize winners. They have come from laboratories on either side of the Iron Curtain, their sole purpose being to seek ways of lessening international tensions. After the conferences, the scientists have attempted, with varying degrees of success, to communicate to their political leaders the ideas that have been discussed; more than one of those ideas, including the proposal for a partial test ban, has become the official policy of their governments. The Pugwash participants aren't always the same (though some are veterans of as many as six meetings), but the average number has been about fifty, and it isn't likely to go much higher, partly because the delegates don't want things to get too cumbersome and partly because the Pugwash movement, as it has come to be known, is operated on a shoestring. The first several conferences were underwritten by Cyrus Eaton, the Cleveland industrialist—it was at his summer place in Pugwash that the original one was held—but in 1959 American members of the Pugwash Continuing Committee, which schedules the gatherings and issues invitations, announced that "as Mr. Eaton has come to play an increasingly active and controversial role in political affairs, the scientists felt that his exclusive support of their conferences may place them in a wrong light." Since then, although Mr. Eaton has continued to contribute, the great majority of participants have either paid their own way or had their expenses defrayed to varying extents by foundations,

READY TO GO

One of America's arsenal of intercontinental ballistic missiles. The one shown here in launching position is capable of delivering a warhead on target more than 6,300 miles away. (Chap. 6)

FROM ALDERMASTON
TO UNITED NATIONS
VIA LONDON
平
和
PATIENTS OF "A" B
SEND THEIR
THE HIROSHIMA
PEACE PILG

facing page
BAN-THE-BOMB PROTEST
Aldermaston marchers reach London
after walking fifty miles.
Two survivors of the attack
on Hiroshima are in the lead.
(Chap. 2)

above
CURTAINLESS CONFERENCE
Russian, Chinese, British,
American, Australian
—scientists from both sides
of the Iron Curtain assembled
in Quebec to collaborate on ideas
for halting the arms race.
(Photo by Mrs. Cyrus Eaton) (Chap. 5)

SECRETARY McNAMARA'S
FORMULA FOR ENOUGHNESS

As the Secretary himself jotted it down
while talking with the author:
Enough = the am't req'd to deter a Sov strike
+ the am't needed to minimize
damage to this country in the
event of a strike (Chap. 6)

Enough = the am't req'd to deter a Sov strike
+ the am't needed to minimize
damage to this country in the
event of a strike

individual donors, or, in the case of Communist participants, national scientific agencies.

❦

I attended a Pugwash Conference in the fall of 1963 that was held in the ancient walled town of Dubrovnik, Yugoslavia, on the Adriatic coast halfway between Venice and Athens. I owed my presence there to an invitation from the Pugwash Continuing Committee on behalf of the scientists and scholars who were temporarily abandoning their formal studies of nature and other fields to convene as a kind of parliament without portfolio. There were participants from twenty-four countries, including the Soviet Union, the United States, Great Britain, East and West Germany, Ghana, India, and Brazil. The Communist Chinese, whose scientists had been at previous meetings, had sent a carefully worded message to the Continuing Committee to the effect that they would not be coming this time; the Chinese academic year, it seemed, was just starting and all their scientists were needed at home for teaching duties.

The conference went on for five days, with the local arrangements taken care of by the Council of Yugoslav Academies, a national organization of learned societies. All of us were put up at a hotel on the outskirts of town called the Neptun, which, as time went by, revealed a susceptibility to power failures. The weather was hardly conducive to cerebrating about the world's troubles. The sky was almost perpetually unclouded, and a bluish haze lay torpidly on the flat Adriatic. The only thing that could possibly be construed as a reminder of the work at hand was a booming of artillery each morning—the guns being fired by the crew of an American movie with a Second World War plot, which was being made in the mountains nearby. The delegates needed no such reminders, though. They just couldn't get enough, it seemed, of such topics as atom-free zones, the test-ban treaty, problems of detection, the abolition of delivery systems, and—the most formidable topic of all—general and complete disarmament, which English-speaking delegates referred to breezily as "g.c.d." The colloquy began at breakfast—no matter what table one drew in the crowded dining room, one found the delegates hard at it—and it went on through the sipping of nightcaps on the Neptun's broad terrace; it persisted in the big buses that carried us daily over a winding road to the conference hall, in Dubrovnik proper; and it displaced small talk at the various receptions tendered in honor of the Pugwashers. "I wish we all had more time together," Dr. Franklin A. Long, a professor of chemistry at Cornell, who for two years had been Assistant Director for Science and Technology of the United States Arms Control and Disarmament Agency, remarked to me. "There are men with incredible brains here, and you're not seeing them at their best. If only they'd been able to do their homework properly!" Another delegate had a plan to guarantee that they did nothing but their homework, by devoting their full time to disarmament studies. He wasn't a scientist himself, but a politician—the Right Honorable Philip Noel-Baker, M.P., a zestful, jaunty man in his middle seventies, who had won the Nobel Peace Prize in 1959 for his work in the field of international relations and disarmament, and who, incidentally, had been captain of the British Olympic team at Antwerp in 1920. "Scientists responded brilliantly to the crisis of the last war, and I believe they could deal just as effectively with this Cold War we have on our hands," Noel-Baker told me one afternoon while we were sharing a bus seat. "They're immensely able as a class. The changes they've made in our lives! Why, when I was a boy most people had no phone and no electricity, and my father had the third automobile to travel the streets of London."

There were times, of course, when the scientists actually were scheduled to discuss atom-free zones, delivery systems, and the rest. These were during their sessions at the conference hall, which was really an art museum, the Umjetnicka Galerija, whose high-ceilinged, chandelier-lit exhibition rooms had, through the good offices of the Council of Yugoslav Academies, been turned over to the conference both for plenary sessions and for the smaller meetings of so-called working groups. (One working group met at the Neptun whenever possible, because several of its members suffered from various infirmities and wanted to spare themselves the bus trips to the museum.) It was at the plenary sessions, I thought, that the general earnestness was most evident. The delegates would give their attention completely to the speaker of the moment, who, microphone in hand, addressed them from a platform that was also occupied by the conference's presiding committee, made up of five or six scientists of different nationalities. Only occasionally was there whispering among the audience, whose members sat facing the platform at two long, parallel tables covered with dark-green cloth. Usually, as they listened intently to papers being read or to greetings being relayed from the heads of various governments—including the United States and the Soviet Union—they took notes, stared thoughtfully at the room's white plaster walls, on which hung a number of indifferent abstractions, or gazed through a broad open window at a prospect of cacti and palms and, beyond this, the Adriatic's gelatinous calm. Most of the participants wore earphones, through which they heard the speaker's words translated by interpreters in a booth at the rear of the room; some, I noticed, had brought along dictionaries with which to check the translations.

Aware though I was of the idea back of the Pugwash movement, I still experienced a certain sense of unreality at seeing so many eminent scientists holding political court in a Balkan museum. There were, among others, Sir John Cockcroft, a nuclear physicist in his sixties, with the features of a professorial Ed Wynn, whose normal precincts are at Cambridge, where he is Master of Churchill College, and who was a recipient of a Nobel Prize in 1951; Professor P. M. S. Blackett, another Nobel laureate (Physics, 1948), whose professional habitat is the Imperial College of Science and Technology in London, where he is Pro-Rector; Professor I. I. Rabi, of Columbia University, a contemporary of Sir John's and of Blackett's, who won the Nobel Prize for Physics in 1944; Professor

Francis Perrin, head of the French Atomic Energy Commission, a short, amiable physicist with an elegant goatee; Professor Leopold Infeld, a theoretical physicist at the University of Warsaw, who was once a close collaborator of Einstein's; Professor Bernard T. Feld, of the Physics Department of M.I.T., who was the chairman of the committee of the American Academy of Arts and Sciences which organized American participation in the conference; Professor Leo Szilard, the co-discoverer, with the late Professor Enrico Fermi, of the principles of the plutonium pile; Professor M. G. K. Menon, a physicist from the Tata Institute of Fundamental Research, in Bombay; D. K. Abbiw-Jackson, of the Kwame Nkrumah University of Science and Technology, in Kumasi, Ghana, a young mathematician with the springy gait of a sprinter; Academician V. A. Kirillin, a tall physicist with the demeanor of a genial schoolmaster, who is vice-president of the Presidium of the Soviet Academy of Sciences, the U.S.S.R.'s highest scientific body; another Soviet Academician, N. N. Bogolubov, who is a theoretical physicist of world renown; Major General N. A. Talensky, a Soviet military theoretician who writes for two publications, *War Thought* and *Red Star;* and Soviet Academician A. N. Tupelov, the famous designer of Soviet aircraft, a portly old man with two Orders of Lenin on his ample chest, who sat pensively through the plenary sessions.

The content of the discussions, both inside and outside the museum, was shaped largely by twenty or so papers on disarmament that the scientists had prepared in advance. Not a single one of these papers that I heard or read failed to mention international suspicion. (The conference itself was not devoid of suspicion; it was possible at various times to hear Western scientists wondering aloud whether Eastern ones were independent spirits or government hacks pushing a Party line, and to hear Eastern scientists expressing similar doubts.) One of the papers was bluntly entitled "Cheating in a Disarmed World." It was the work of Professor R. R. Neild, of Britain's National Institute of Economic and Social Research, and it examined the widely held fear that the concept of disarmament is a delusion because one nuclear power or another would surely conceal bombs from internationally appointed inspectors. Neild, however, didn't think cheating would be easy in a disarmed world—a thesis he chose to develop by simulating the thought processes of theoretical cheating statesmen, whom he categorized as "gambling robots who have no purpose in life other than to destroy their enemies." Such robots would certainly be confronted by dilemmas, Neild asserted. Supposing, he speculated, one country were to threaten another with bombs that it had concealed from the disarmament inspectors. Why wouldn't it occur to the cheater that his intended victim might also have cheated? And why wouldn't he also worry lest he arouse the antagonism of unthreatened governments, whose ranks, for all he knew, might also include a cheater or two? "Those who argue that a threat by a cheater would work seem either to have failed to think through the problem or else to have made asymmetrical assumptions when doing so,"

Neild declared. "That is, they have assumed that one side, because of superior political morals, would never cheat, and that the other side would recognize this virtue and, as a result of inferior political morals, would take advantage of it by cheating and threatening to attack. I have never seen these assumptions spelt out and justified. . . . Whatever one's views about the morals of either side, it is hard to see either side crediting the other with superior honesty." Neild went on to show in detail the headaches that cheaters would have to face if, instead of merely making threats, they contemplated a surprise attack. He went so far as to doubt whether a surprise attack would even be possible in a disarmed world. At this point, he parted company with his "gambling robots," calling them a pet abstraction of "strategic analysts who postulate creatures of tireless aggression." By the time disarmament accords were reached, according to Neild's reasoning, Communist and non-Communist leaders alike would have had to sell their public so hard on the unthinkability of nuclear war as a method of settling disputes that the prevailing political climate would be one such as we can hardly even imagine today. A climate of that sort, said Neild, could be achieved only gradually, and the same would be true of its reversal; that is, cheating, if it were to occur, would come not as a surprise but as the climax of a period of diplomatic warnings, attempts at conciliation, and, of course, heightened vigilance in inspection. "What you may suffer if the [disarmament] Treaty goes wrong is disappointment, not disaster," Neild concluded. "Disaster is what you may suffer if you don't make a treaty."

The papers varied greatly not only in their topics but in their tone and in their reasoning, ranging from the abstruse to the simple and everyday. One of them, entitled "A Role for Small Nations," written by Professor O. Kofoed-Hansen, a nuclear physicist at the Risø Research Laboratory, near Copenhagen, leaned heavily on a fairy tale by Hans Christian Andersen. Kofoed-Hansen held that it was the duty of small countries like his own to be as outspoken about the follies of "the two big camps" as was the boy in "The Emperor's New Clothes," who saw that the emperor was naked and said so. "Can the small countries learn to behave like Hans Christian Andersen's small child?" Kofoed-Hansen asked. "I hope they can, because they and their men are not so much hampered by fear of losing face and position, because they have less of it to start with."

A scientist from another small country, Austria, suggested an experiment for which, he believed, certain small countries could serve as "pilot plants." The countries he had in mind were European neutrals whose borders were not in dispute, and the heart of his proposal was embodied in a rhetorical question: "What will happen to this country if it disarms unilaterally and proclaims itself to be a test case of the possibility of peaceful coexistence?" The proponent of the experiment was Professor Hans Thirring, a short, genial man in his seventies, who is a professor of physics at the University of Vienna and a member of the Vienna Academy of Sciences, and is a revered public figure in his country. If nothing else, Thirring said, the small countries would be saved the expense of supporting their "rather inadequate conventional forces." Economics would figure in the broader aspects of his experiment, too, he pointed out, for the United States and Russia, when each saw that the other had refrained from gobbling up the small countries, would come to feel easy enough about each other to do away with their staggering military budgets. This, Thirring predicted, would free vast amounts of manpower and capital with which the rivals could each show off their own systems to best advantage—a form of competition that would not cost the world its life. In casting about for likely "pilot plants," the Professor ruled out Switzerland and Sweden, on the ground that they had made so much of their armed neutrality for so long that "the idea of being a soldierly nation is a kind of 'ersatz' for the missed occasions to have fought glorious wars." The physicist ended up by nominating Finland, Ireland, and Austria to lead the way in total disarmament. He was particularly keen about his own country's fitness for this role, observing that "Austrians are not frustrated by lack of recent military glory, having fought bravely dozens of big battles and lost all wars in the last two and a half centuries."

A number of papers used technical language to make their political points. One author—a theoretical physicist from the Netherlands—sounded a little too theoretical to me. He saw the international situation in terms of a feedback system, illustrating his concept with diagrams whose components—International Tension and Distrust, Level of Armaments, External Political Influences—were connected by curving arrows that stood for Cause and Effect. "Feedback systems," he told a plenary session, "may be stable or not, depending on the value of the parameters characterizing the system. It seems that at present the system of the international situation is not really unstable (at least it does not show a *fast* exponential runaway), although positive feedback probably causes appreciable feedback amplification. But it should be stressed that a relatively small change of the parameters of the system, due to a technological change, might cause the system to become unstable. . . ."

Sir John Cockcroft, for his part, delivered a paper that was both technical and readily intelligible. He took up the matter of improving methods for the detection of underground nuclear experiments, saying he believed that such improvements might facilitate agreement on a complete nuclear-test-ban treaty. Speaking of the recently negotiated partial test-ban treaty, he said that thanksgiving was in order for the fact that "the political sense of our leaders" had not heeded "the lunatic fringe of science," which was ever on the lookout for "more exotic types of nuclear weapons." Sir John didn't think that underground shots could contribute much to weapons development anyway, but he felt that if they were continued, some countries might come to fear that "the present balance of weapons technology" was being upset, and might exercise their right to withdraw from the treaty now in force. Sir John then reviewed recent progress in seismology, saying he believed that since 1958 the methods for the detection of underground explosions at distances of between roughly twenty-five hundred and six thousand miles had been improved thirty to fifty times. The central problem, he said, was still that of distinguishing earthquakes from explosions, and here he delivered a disquisition on the behavior of various underground shock waves, his general point being that the seismological signal for even a shallow earthquake was much stronger than that for a man-made explosion. After citing other criteria, he said that Russian and American scientists were in considerable agreement on the issue of underground detection. Their chief difference, he noted, was over the number of on-site inspections needed for checking "suspicious events," and this difference had been narrowed down to a point where Soviet negotiators believed that three inspections were sufficient and their American counterparts favored seven. "Because of the uncertainty of the data," Sir John said, "both numbers were scientifically reasonable, and . . . the actual number of inspections would have to be decided politically." He then ticked off a series of suggestions for making the data less uncertain, among them the use of unmanned seismic stations in regions of high seismic activity; the burying of seismographs in holes drilled to a depth of about ten thousand feet; and the placing of such equipment on the ocean bed. Of course, Sir John concluded, there was a limit to the scientific improvements that could be made in detection, but that before that limit was reached, Russian, American, and British scientists should do everything in their power to compose their technical differences.

❦

Unlike the plenary sessions, the meetings of the working groups were small and informal, with much of the atmosphere of seminars. There were five such groups, in each of which groups of scientists, varying in number from day to day, examined a particular topic. I sat in on one that was listed as "Working Group 5: The Partial Test Ban, the Problem of Detection, and the Next Steps." Its chairman was Alexander Rich, an M.I.T. professor of biophysics, and present at its meetings at various times were Cockcroft, Blackett, Rabi, Long, a young Harvard associate professor of biology named Matthew Meselson, and Academician L. A. Artsimovich, a short, broad-shouldered theoretical physicist, with brown, intent eyes, who was a member of the Presidium of the Soviet Academy of Sciences and Academic Secretary of its Department of Physicomathematical Sciences. The group's job was to examine the obstacles in the way of broadening the present partial test-ban treaty, and, along with the other working groups, to draft recommendations for submission to the final plenary session.

One obstacle that couldn't very well be examined was Red China's opposition to a test-ban treaty, since no one from that country was on hand.

"Would somebody care to act as an honorary Chinese?" Rich inquired at one point.

"Such an interesting psychology such a somebody would have to have," Artsimovich said, in his strongly accented English.

It was far simpler to consider some of the attitudes behind France's recalcitrance, for now Rich had only to invite a French delegate to step in and tell us about it. The Frenchman turned out to be Father Dominique Dubarle, a Dominican priest who is a professor of the philosophy of science at the Catholic University in Paris; his specialty is mathematical logic, and he has also done nuclear research at the Ecole Polytechnique. Father Dubarle wasn't at all sure that the government of France would forever refuse to sign a test-ban treaty. For one thing, he said, a public-opinion poll had indicated that half of France did not share General de Gaulle's view of the present treaty. As for the General's hope of developing hydrogen bombs, Father Dubarle said, such weapons weren't expected to be tested for a few years at the earliest, so there was time in which to enlist further public support for a change in French policy. The point that had to be driven home to his countrymen, he went on, was that the money spent on nuclear weapons could be better used for raising the standard of living; French scientists and thinkers, he believed, should disseminate this idea. He characterized those leading the drive for hydrogen bombs as strong-willed people who didn't want France looked down upon by other nuclear powers; General de Gaulle was hardly alone in his dreams of French glory, for in the opinion poll about a third of those who favored France's remaining in the arms race had given "prestige" as their reason. "It is so easy to imitate," Father Dubarle said, glancing at his Russian, American, and British colleagues. "It is the path of least resistance."

Despite endless hours spent in arguing the wisdom and the wording of this or that memorandum, the members of the working group engaged in no outright ideological quarrels. The nearest they came to one was when Dr. Long urged that the group go on record as favoring a program of research in underground detection techniques, to be conducted jointly by American, British, and Soviet scientists.

"Jointly?" Artsimovich asked at once, blinking. "But that's like a professor making a partner of a pupil. You have been so much more interested in seismology than we—you have had ninety-eight underground tests to our two."

No one disputed Artsimovich's point, but after a moment Long, who is a Montanan with a friendly manner, reiterated his thought.

Rabi said, "Anything that carries forward the good will generated by the test-ban treaty is all to the good. I think Long's idea falls in this category."

Artsimovich didn't seem to be listening. His eyes were shut, and his head was rocking slightly from side to side. When he looked at his colleagues again, he spoke with an impatient openness. He didn't suppose that Long's proposal would do any harm, he said, but he didn't really see that it would do much good. Everything they were talking about, he said, hinged on an American overconcern with on-site inspections and on his country's resistance to the idea of what it considered too many inspections. The solution, said Artsimovich, had to do with a mutually acceptable number of inspections, as Sir John's paper had suggested, but how did one arrive at such a figure? The Russian recalled that at the Pugwash Conference in 1962, in London, a small group of Russian and American scientists had gone off by themselves, determined to lick the problem on a strictly scientific basis. But it hadn't worked. The Russians' calculations had led them to the conclusion that one inspection annually would be sufficient; the Americans had come up with fifty as their figure. Both answers could be defended scientifically, Artsimovich said, depending on how suspicious one considered "suspicious events." If one wanted each and every suspicious event investigated, he explained, that would mean from fifty to seventy inspections, but if one assumed, as most scientists did, that only a *series* of underground tests could have military significance, then the number of inspections need be nowhere near that high. "There is no simple relationship between the number of inspections, on the one hand, and the number of suspicious events, on the other," Artsimovich told Working Group 5. "That is what the scientific point of view shows us. Everything depends not on jointly improving detection techniques but on trust and confidence."

❦

Between sessions at the museum, the delegates, I found, were sometimes willing to talk about themselves and about why they had seen fit to leave their labs and come to Dubrovnik. One of those scientists who talked to me about this and related matters was Professor Arne Engström, a tall, blue-eyed Swede who is a cell physiologist and biophysicist at the Karolinska Institutet, a medical-research center in Stockholm, and who is also a member of many Swedish government committees, including one that helps choose Nobel Prize winners. "The day of the ivory tower is over for scientists," he said as we sat at a table on the Neptun terrace having a beer. He added that he wasn't really sure there had ever been such a day. More likely, he conjectured, the wider implications of scientific work had gone unrecognized by the public, by governments, and by the scientists themselves. Nowadays, though, science and technology had become the most superficial sort of status symbol. He told me that he had recently been impressed by this during a flight aboard a Sudanese plane. "It was a big, sleek, shiny jet with all the trimmings," he said. "I wondered why the Sudanese, who aren't usually in a hurry, should have gone to such unnecessary expense. The only answer I could think of was that they wanted to put their best foot forward for all the world to see." It was modern weapons, of course, that had changed everything, he went on, including his own country's concept of neutrality. Sweden, he said, could no longer wait for a war to demonstrate its traditional neutrality. She felt that she had to be neutral in advance, so to speak, and for that reason he and other Swedish scientists were engaged in a vast "protection-research" program, involving deep shelters, inhalation masks, and other civil-defense measures. Professor Engström eyed his glass of beer. "Another thing—a Danish friend of mine has told me that practically any brewery can be turned into a production center for cholera toxins," he said. "Just throw up some barbed wire and post a few guards, my friend told me, and you have a military emplacement that can wipe out thousands. The scientist's chief moral concern today, I believe, is the creation of just such potentialities. The difficulty is that the matter isn't always as black-and-white as the conversion of breweries. In science, one man does basic research and another puts it to practical use. Where does accountability lie? There's the gamble, and I know it well. A year ago, as you know, the Nobel Prize was given to a research team for bringing about a deeper understanding of the genetic code, of the mechanism of heredity. Well, I was the man who presented the case for that research to the Nobel Prize committee, and all the time I was analyzing the achievement, I was thinking, My God, what am I doing? In ten years, this research can make dogs of the human race."

Father Dubarle talked with me shortly after he had briefed Working Group 5. This wasn't his first Pugwash Conference, he said as we shared a bench outside the hotel—nor, he hoped, would it be his last. It was his belief that the Pugwash movement was helping scientists become intelligent in a "universal" way. Problems of the kind that we are now up against, he said, don't lend themselves to a nationalistic approach—although, he added with a smile, he wasn't sure he hadn't encountered just such an approach at the Pugwash meeting in 1958 in Kitzbühel,

Austria. "A Soviet colleague, seeing how I was dressed, walked up to me and asked, 'Are you an observer for the Vatican?' When I explained what I did in France, he said, 'That's odd. We have monks in my country, but none of them are scientists.'" Not many decades ago, Father Dubarle continued, science itself was beset by nationalism—people spoke of a "German science" and a "French science," and so on, and each variety had its boosters and detractors. But that narrow view had largely disappeared, and this, in Father Dubarle's opinion, was all to the good, since he himself thought of science as "creating a world community of knowledge." Politically, though, he said, the issue at present was "to create a world community of generosity," and it was in this area, he believed, that meetings like the Pugwash Conferences might bear fruit. "Scientists have much to learn about politics," Father Dubarle said. "We are not yet nearly as realistic about politics as we are about nature. But there, of course, we have a good method of investigation that has evolved over centuries. If we want to learn about fundamental particles, for example, we use that method for organizing our experiments. But just because we have no such method for dealing with political problems doesn't mean that we shouldn't try to solve them. Perhaps, if we are granted the time, we may even create a political method."

"Do you think that guilt brings some scientists to the Pugwash Conferences?" I asked.

"Yes, but I think there is much more of a feeling of responsibility than guilt," he replied. "Certainly we have our sins, but the one good thing that we can do by way of expiation for the bomb is to bring about a new type of social atmosphere."

❦

I was especially curious to hear the views of scientists with Communist backgrounds. Perhaps the Soviet delegation included a political watchdog or two, but none of the Russians I happened to talk with sounded like one. Certainly Academician Artsimovich didn't, one day when he and I lunched together at the Neptun.

"What qualifications do you think scientists have for forming judgments on political matters?" I asked him.

"We have one or two good features," he replied. "We have a comparatively high degree of honesty. That comes from our scientific style of thinking, which is carried on without reference to the opinions of other men. And we are comparatively independent, which also comes from our scientific training. We direct our thought to the problem we are working on. We are not easily distracted—comparatively, I mean." Artsimovich laughed. "One further thing," he said. "We are not paid for these qualities. If we were, they would disappear at once."

A moment later, another quality without monetary reward occurred to him. "I think we are better educated than politicians," he said. "I am here, so take me for an example. I think I know more about philosophy, history, and geography than most politicians. Do you think most politicians are able to imagine what would have happened if General Burgoyne had not surrendered at Saratoga? Do you think they know who killed Henry IV of France for recognizing the religious rights of the Huguenots? Or the name of the general who led the charge on Cemetery Ridge at Gettysburg?" It was possible, Artsimovich went on, that scientists were a bit cocky about their ability to solve political problems. "This century has seen a whole realignment of natural scientists and social scientists," he said. "We natural scientists have become too self-assured since the bomb. There has been a sudden surge for us to levels of high importance."

I mentioned that an increasing number of social scientists had been coming to Pugwash Conferences, and Artsimovich made a face. Generally speaking, he said, he found social scientists a pretty ineffective bunch. "Gatherers of material," he said. "Fifty years ago, Professor Rutherford, the great British physicist, said that scientists were divided into two categories—physicists and stamp collectors."

The Russian shut his eyes, and then shrugged as he opened them.

"We scientists have become like gypsies," he said. "We wander from conference to conference, trying to find roads to peace, acting as voluntary advisers to our political leaders. We know better than anyone else what there is to be concerned about, so it is possible that, without trying to, we have become the most peaceful people in the world."

Another Soviet Academician I talked with was B. M. Vul, a stocky Ukrainian with a cordial manner, who was probably a few years older than Artsimovich.

I asked Vul, who is an experimental physicist, if he didn't think that the conflicting ideologies of his country and the West hindered the Pugwash deliberations.

He shook his head. "We are discussing here survival, and without that there can be no ideologies of any kind," he said. "It is for always bearing in mind such a purpose that the discipline of the scientific method is especially valuable."

"Doesn't the scientific method require controlled conditions?" I asked.

"Yes," he replied. "In my laboratory, I create the conditions. I decide the temperatures and pressures. But with politics, I find a fixed condition, so what do I do? I try to apply the method I already know not only to deal with the issues that are pressing but to develop and extend the method, so that it can deal with supposedly uncontrollable factors. With nature, this approach has often helped us to discover the behavior of factors that were thought to be uncontrollable."

I asked him if he thought scientists could help matters by refusing to devise any more weapons. It was too late for that, Vul answered; too many weapons were already in existence. Like Father Dubarle, he thought that only a change in the social atmosphere could produce a true peace. "In my opinion," he said, "scientists have some influence with politicians, and this is fortunate, because scientists trust each other. We deal with objects and we try to be objective. For politicians, the world cannot always be so real. When politicians meet, each assumes the other is a liar."

Finally, there was Academician A. A. Blagonravov, a silvery-haired engineer with thick gray brows, who, I was told, is a leading figure in his country's space activities. ("You might almost say he was the Communist space czar," one American delegate had said.) With the aid of a Soviet interpreter, Blagonravov and I chatted over tea during a half-hour break at the museum.

The conference, Blagonravov said, was meeting in a congenial atmosphere, coming, as it did, so soon after the signing of the partial test-ban treaty; other Pugwash Conferences had met at less fortunate times.

I mentioned the fact that some military men in the United States had been opposed to the partial test-ban treaty, and inquired if this had also been true in the Soviet Union.

Blagonravov said that he himself had not heard of any such opposition, and he reminded me that the highest-ranking military men in his country were members of the Communist Party, which meant that they adhered strictly to its political decisions.

I asked Blagonravov if he thought that those in the Soviet delegation had a sense of guilt about weapons work they might have done.

"No, I do not think this is true of the delegation," Blagonravov said, speaking slowly to the interpreter. "But perhaps your question could apply to me personally, because in the last war I developed an automatic weapon that was widely used. I do not know how many lives it took, but when I saw the consequences of the war, I was determined not to take part in weapons work again. I am not doing so now. I am in space research. My special interest in it has to do with automation."

Blagonravov smiled when I inquired why he had chosen to come to Dubrovnik.

"I like being with scientists," he told me. "I prefer it to being with diplomats, with whom I have also been many times." Blagonravov waited for the interpreter to finish translating this, then said, in a changed tone, "I am a member of society, that is why I am here. We scientists want to stay alive, the same as everyone else. We have work to do."

❦

At the final plenary session, which was held in the late afternoon, the chairmen of the working groups submitted their committees' proposals for acceptance by the whole conference. No pitched battles developed between East and West in the discussions that followed. There was no trading of ideological slogans. There were arguments, among them some between fellow-members of delegations, including the Soviet delegation. All the recommendations were weighed with the utmost gravity—so much so that one might have thought the proceedings were those of a deliberative body vested with political power. It was, however, precisely the lack of such power that kept the scientists from appearing self-important. In the absence of that power, as far as I was concerned, there was nothing to do but remember that they were intellectual men voluntarily using their intellects in behalf of a complex and uncertain cause.

Pretty nearly all the proposals were accepted,

including that of Dr. Long's group for a joint seismological study. (At the last meeting of Working Group 5, Artsimovich had decided to go along with it.) A number of other recommendations came from the working groups. One of them was that the International Atomic Energy Agency, in Vienna, be authorized forthwith to keep fissile material for power reactors from being diverted to the manufacture of weapons. "Production of fissile material in nuclear-power technology now surpasses that for weapons use," the recommendation stated. "Thus, the essential material base for nuclear-bomb production is arising at many points throughout the world.... With the rapid growth of nuclear-power reactors, little time is left to establish a pattern of responsible use that would provide protection to all countries against the diversion of plutonium to nuclear weapons...." Another recommendation sought to forestall surprise attacks by conventional armed forces in Central Europe through the establishment of international control posts at major transportation centers inside the NATO and the Warsaw Pact countries; observers at such posts would be able to sound warnings if large numbers of men and arms were massed. This plan also included a proposal that military men from each side, with facilities for rapid communication with their governments, be stationed with the troops of the other side.

One working group proposed that strong inducements be offered in order to get countries to refuse to make nuclear weapons. Such nations, its recommendation stated, should be guaranteed the protection of the great powers, within the framework of the United Nations, and should also be given access to all the scientific knowledge they might have gained from the production of nuclear weapons. Another working group urged the establishment of a new, permanent International Disarmament Organization to oversee the process of disarmament and its subsequent control; the agency would guard not only against actual cheating but against the fear of such cheating. "Since no inspection system can be perfect," the proposal declared, "greater efforts might profitably be made to devise machinery to deal openly with the doubts and fears which must inevitably arise from time to time."

The list of ideas went on and on. There was no telling what might come of any particular one of them. Perhaps nothing would. Perhaps the scientists would decide that they should refine it further at a future conference. Or perhaps, as has happened in the past, it would next come up in some august international forum, sponsored by a Foreign Minister. Whatever their final disposition, the proposals that were being put forth in the art museum were so many additions to a treasury that statesmen could draw on whenever the strange flux of international relations made it possible. "I can't prove it," Artsimovich said to me, just as he was leaving to return to Russia, "but without conferences like this one, it would be harder than it is to imagine that things are going to be better."

6
An Inquiry into Enoughness

The great, and conceivably the final, commonplace of our time is that nuclear war is unthinkable, and yet, as heads of state keep telling us, the weapons that make such a catastrophe possible continue to be turned out daily in the United States and in Russia (and, at a far slower tempo, in Great Britain, France, and, presumably, China). Once begun anywhere, stockpiles of this formidable ordnance have done nothing but grow, following a pattern that has prevailed ever since the first atomic bomb was put together, nearly twenty years ago. As world leaders have also repeatedly told us, there are "devices" in existence now that are thousands of times as powerful as the two that were detonated over Japan in 1945. We hear, too, of "low-yield" weapons—"refined" or "sophisticated" models—that military men consider ideally suited to such "tactical" pursuits as the taking of a bridge or a beachhead. (Certain of these models have forty times the yield of the Hiroshima bomb, which is now categorized as "nominal" in size.) There are now on routine patrols planes each of which is armed with bombs whose combined potency is the equivalent of all the firepower expended in the Second World War; this is less than half the firepower of a single one of the Polaris submarines that lie ready for action at the bottom of the sea. The chiefs of the nuclear governments bluntly state that there can be no perfect defense against incoming rockets. Repeatedly, in pleading for disarmament, these personages have declared that the opening minutes of a nuclear war could leave millions of casualties. The broad effect of this steady preachment, delivered for years from the secular pulpits of scattered chancelleries, has been to call forth the question—profoundly and widely, I believe—of just how much is enough when it comes to nuclear weapons. If two "nominal" specimens could do what they did to Hiroshima and Nagasaki, then why the assembly-line production of thousands upon thousands more, every one of them the potential cargo of a missile or a plane capable of travelling at several times the speed of sound? Given the nature of these weapons, I have been asking myself, is it reasonable to imagine that a country can reach the point of deciding that its arsenal is strong enough to see it through any crisis—of feeling that it need no longer concern itself with the comparative strength of rival powers? In short, is it reasonable to imagine that Russia or the United States could choose to resign unilaterally from the present arms race? While the question might apply to either nation, it probably makes more sense to address it to the stronger of the two—which, according to all the intelligence reports that our leaders believe in, is our own. In any event, I have recently put in a fair amount of time in Washington exploring the idea of enoughness, so to speak, with members of the United States government. Among the people with whom I discussed the various aspects of this idea were the Secretary of State, the Secretary of Defense, the Chairman of the Atomic Energy Commission, the Director of the Bureau of the Budget, senators, congressmen, multi-starred generals, and decision-making scientists. And as far as I can make out, the idea of armed sufficiency, in any settled, static form, is a tortuous and elusive one, as hard to define as the state of the world. Wandering the capital in search of elucidation, I grew accustomed to hearing earnest answers that were charged with dilemma and paradox, with fact shaped by opinion, with logic rooted in prayer. Indeed, before I was through, it seemed less a concept that I was looking into than the mentality of a nuclear capital—of a collection of individuals responsible for the country's safety. Much the same state of mind, with all its doubt and dissension, may also be encountered in the other great nuclear capital, I learned from officials who had spent time in Russia.

A number of the officials I talked with, in the Pentagon, on Capitol Hill, and at the State Department, displayed a surprisingly personal reaction when I asked their opinion on what was enough in the way of arms. A scientist with the Arms Control and

Disarmament Agency began his reply with "Don't think for a minute that I'm soft-headed, but . . ." A Regular Army colonel, after inviting me to sit down in his Pentagon office, wanted me to know that he was a devoted family man, the father of four children. "So, whatever I tell you, remember that," he said, and thereupon set forth his belief that the United States needs every last weapon it is capable of manufacturing. It was a viewpoint, incidentally, that was far from universal in the Pentagon. In fact, I met senior officers there who proved to be far more diplomacy-minded than certain officers of the State Department, who were all for solving a political impasse or two around the globe with a few well-aimed conventional bombs. I met numerous "hawks" and "doves"—people with strong views on whether our nuclear stockpiles should go up or down. Few of them, though, were thinking in terms of a fixed level of such armaments, possibly because they were too deeply absorbed in their own positions, or else, as I have suggested, because of the elusiveness—or even the unreality—of any such idea. Some of these partisans, whichever side they were on, sounded as though they were guided less by set convictions than by fear of their opponents' position. One "dove" with whom I talked—a senator's legislative assistant—envied his opponents for having on their side a man with the fierce tenacity of General Curtis LeMay, the Air Force Chief of Staff, an unswerving champion of an all-out weapons buildup. Compared to the General, he said, a certain well-known leader of the "doves" was positively bashful. "Oh, he thinks arms control is important and all that, but he also thinks there are other issues just as important," the legislative assistant told me.

The incessant cross fire of views drove me at one point to seek refuge in the office of the Defense Department's Historian, Dr. Rudolph A. Winnacker, a man of about sixty, who had a genial, professorial detachment that conveyed the impression that the course of history would flow on and on. "Enough? Enough?" he said, reflecting on the subject of my inquiry. "Enough is a matter of circumstances, isn't it? It depends on a nation's ambitions, and on the threats it faces." I asked him whether history couldn't teach us something about the matter of enough, and he smiled benignly. "No, no—please don't take history too seriously," he said. "It's an illusion—the thought that we can perceive the familiar in the past. History does *not* repeat itself. The fact is we have never been more on our own than we are right now, and it's the peculiar power of the atom, combined with the speed of technological change, that has made it so."

❦

Secretary McNamara, a direct, efficient man, believed he had a clear picture of what constituted enough. He described it for me unhesitatingly when I talked to him in his office, and, for emphasis, he wrote it down on a sheet of paper as he spoke. The paper read, "Enough = the amount required to deter a Soviet strike + the amount needed to minimize damage to this country in the event of a strike." The formula was not new to me; in fact, I had already discovered that most government officials subscribed to it, but that it didn't mean the same thing to all of them.

That word "deter" was forever being differently defined, and in my view this was of supreme importance, inasmuch as "deterrence" was the basis of our entire policy—including, of course, any possible American resignation from the arms race. Indeed, as I heard the word invoked again and again, it took on an almost mystical quality, as though it represented a truth revealed in Genesis. Actually, I knew, its use in this context went back no more than four or five years after V-J Day, to the time when Soviet troops in Europe enjoyed a numerical superiority and we retained our nuclear monopoly. A Soviet invasion of the West was feared, and we announced that we would deter any such invasion, even if it meant the use of nuclear arms. Now that we no longer have our monopoly, the original concept of deterrence has altered radically. The doctrine has become essentially psychological, because victory in a nuclear war, according to nearly everyone I met, is largely a mirage. "People talk of 'nuclear superiority,' but that's not synonymous with winning a war, as they imply," Secretary McNamara told me. "As a matter of fact, 'nuclear superiority' is ours this very minute. It makes it possible for us to take a Russian strike and hit back, and although that is a considerable achievement, it is not what I think of as victory."

The Secretary's attitude toward victory is shared by most people in Washington, but some officials—particulary elected ones—doubt whether it has yet been widely accepted by the country at large. One congressman—an Ohioan who is an admirer of Mr. McNamara—told me this was certainly true in his district. "The Department of Defense has become the Department of Retaliation," he said, "but it's asking a lot of Americans to expect them to understand that, even when we seem to be getting along with the Soviets. We were all brought up to believe that America was one country that always won its wars. But beyond that, in my opinion, most people, whether they're Russians or Chinese or Laplanders, have an almost animal-like faith that in a showdown force can always provide the solution."

For Dr. Winnacker, the policy of deterrence had far-reaching historical implications. In his view, it had the effect of making recent events seem like moments in antiquity. "To think," he said, "that as recently as the Second World War ninety per cent of us were able to remain at home, driving our cars, eating in restaurants, and going to the movies, while the government had the power to call for unconditional surrender abroad. And a few decades earlier, in the days of the Ottoman Empire, the skipper of a gunboat could make foreign policy by going ashore to rescue an American citizen. Wars can never again serve as extensions of diplomacy. We have entered a lifelong endurance contest."

❦

"What will deter a Soviet strike? Answer: Unacceptable damage from our surviving forces." These were words that Secretary McNamara wrote down, emphatically, on another sheet of paper during my talk with him. But, like his formula for deterrence, I found, the words meant different things to different officials. This time, it was the phrase "unacceptable damage" that was variously defined, and this again seemed very important, since, I reflected, the casualties we could inflict on a would-be aggressor were, in effect, synonymous with deterrence. The number of such casualties, it seemed to me, had everything to do with the question of enoughness, but the estimates I heard rarely agreed, though they were all appallingly high. Moreover, they were all admittedly speculative—even the ones offered by officials of the highest rank. "What level of destruction is it that will deter?" Dr. Harold B. Brown, the Defense Department's Director of Research and Engineering, asked. "One impact on Moscow or a hundred and fifty million casualties throughout the Soviet Union? I'd call those the extremes, but someone else might consider either one reasonable, depending on his point of view." Another official suggested that the point of enough as far as the Russians' willingness to absorb punishment was concerned would probably not be reached until their losses exceeded the ones they suffered in the Second World War—about twenty million dead. A sub-Cabinet officer believed that the cause of deterrence as it is now being served by both East and West held out the prospect of three hundred million fatalities in the Soviet Union, Western Europe, and the United States. "Definitely unacceptable," he said. "Definitely unacceptable, too, when one takes into account the factor of associated industrial destruction." So high are casualty expectations, I was given to understand, that even if a nuclear attack were to be made on us, we might choose not to respond in kind, lest nuclear hostilities be stepped up to their full potential. This, I learned, is in keeping with the idea of "flexible response," to which the government is at present committed. This flexibility, it was explained to me, permits us to choose among retaliatory measures ranging from a "spasm response," which means hitting back at an attacker with everything we have, to a "controlled response," which means letting the punishment fit the crime. "Even if New York were destroyed, I would want to investigate the reason and motive before responding," one of the most important members of our government informed me. "Would you want us to respond spasmodically to a single insane attack made by one man with one weapon, for instance? Wouldn't you want us to bear in mind the possibility that we would bring about a worldwide holocaust if we were to do such a thing? I am not suggesting for an instant that an attacker would escape punishment. Our response would be swift, but would it need to be so swift that the President would lack time to evaluate the attack and match it? I know that many people doubt whether measured retaliation could ever be practiced, but if it should be practicable, then our duty, I believe, would be to try to keep any conflict down to a level that, however tragic, was not apocalyptic."

All of the people I talked with assured me that the human species was destined to survive, come what might. Not one of them, whether a "dove" or a "hawk," took much stock in the notion of "overkill"—the assertion that there are already many more than enough nuclear weapons in existence to wipe out the entire populations of the Soviet Union and the United States. ("Why wouldn't things be bad enough anyway?" one man at the Arms Control and Disarmament Agency asked me.) "Overkill" was generally dismissed, I found, as logistically specious. The "overkill" theorists, employing the Hiroshima bomb as a unit of measurement, assume that for every twenty kilotons of nuclear explosive—the power of the Hiroshima bomb—there would be a hundred thousand casualties, which was approximately the number killed in the Japanese city. Thus, one megaton of nuclear explosives would produce five million casualties. Once this premise is accepted, there is nothing to do but add up the supposed megatonnage in nuclear arsenals, which, as everyone knows, now equals many, many times twenty kilotons—or, for that matter, twenty megatons. "By this chain of reasoning, the 'overkill' people could claim that the existence of a single bomb of a hundred megatons would prove their theory, and that's patently impossible," I was told by a senator who leaned to the side of the "doves." "Besides, their calculations are based on what would happen to cities of a hundred thousand or over, and don't allow for people living in sparsely settled areas. Still, as a catchword, rather than a concept, 'overkill' is hard to beat. I know I've been tempted to use it that way more than once."

Perhaps the most authoritative assurance that the species is safe from extinction was given me by General Glenn A. Kent, of the Defense Department's

Office of Research and Engineering, who has drawn the grim assignment of projecting the likely casualty tolls in the United States from various types of enemy attacks. General Kent, a quiet-spoken, pleasant man, told me, "Even if we did nothing to protect ourselves, enemy attacks would be unlikely to kill more than seventy per cent of the American people. That's where we find the curve of our graph flattens out. Strong diminishing returns set in there, you see, and that's a law that the Russians can't repeal any more than we can. Naturally, the more protection we had, the higher our survival rate would be. With an efficient system of civilian defense—and, of course, some ballistic-missile defense—we might save seventy per cent or more of our society—and by 'society' I mean the viability of the country. Some people claim that if we were to get below a certain survival threshold, we couldn't ever recover, but in my opinion that threshold would be represented by a very, very low figure. The number of survivors certainly wouldn't be anywhere near as low as the number of Pilgrims who landed at Plymouth, and look at what that small number was able to do with this country in a comparatively short time."

❦

"We have tens of thousands of bombs, but if only we had just a single way of telling when we'll ever have enough of those horrible things!" Senator John O. Pastore, of Rhode Island, said to me. "We're up against the fear of the unknown, and it makes us suspect we have too little when all the time we may have far too much. How long do you suppose we can go on the way we're going?" The Senator, who is chairman of the Joint Congressional Committee on Atomic Energy, was discussing still another facet of enoughness—the question of whether we possess the patience and forbearance to go on indefinitely adhering to a policy whose triumph lies in the preservation of a "terroristic peace" (as General Austin W. Betts, of Army Research and Development, had called it when I talked to him). Like many of his colleagues, Senator Pastore saw deterrence as a mosaic of precarious details and assumptions, every one of which must be kept carefully in place, lest (as the Russians also theorize) a glaring weakness prove irresistible to a would-be aggressor. It seemed to the Senator to demand unending alertness—the whole distracting, expensive process of contriving a proper "mix" of conventional and nuclear weapons, small and big, in order to present the Communists with a "credible deterrent." This term, which I heard frequently, refers to our having a "family" of weapons so variegated that the Communists could not doubt, as it is sometimes thought that they may, our disposition and ability to employ violence whether the action required should be limited or all out in scope. As Secretary McNamara testified in the winter of 1964 before the House Armed Services Committee, "The greater our variety of weapons, the more political choices we can make in any given situation."

The claims on our endurance of which Senator Pastore spoke are everywhere apparent, a stark and now familiar vista. The bombs and missiles, the submarines and newly developed tactical weapons, all stand for such claims, and so, of course, do the defense plants in which millions of men are earning a livelihood. So do the vast numbers of men in uniform—each of whom, as an Air Force major observed to me, can accomplish his mission "only if he never does what he's been trained for." Moreover, I was often told, the longer we hold to our present course, the more binding grows our commitment to deterrence—a word that, it might be mentioned, some officials consider simply a euphemism for "arms race." Certainly our nuclear stockpiles must tend to have such a binding effect, for their longevity, it appears, is almost as impressive as their potency. "Nuclear materials aren't products that go away," I was informed by Spurgeon Keeny, of the United States Office of Science and Technology. "They're not like tanks or planes, whose life expectancy is ten to twenty years. They're made of uranium 235 and plutonium, and that stuff lasts forever, as far as I'm concerned. Plutonium has only lost half of its power after twenty-four thousand years, and as for uranium 235, the period is seven hundred million years." The plants turning out our nuclear weapons are another binding factor. Their capacity, I was told, had been set at formidable levels in the somewhat panicky months immediately after we discovered that our nuclear monopoly was gone. Production quotas were considered not only high but unattainable, though they proved not to be so. Costs, too, were overestimated, as it developed, which inflated both the government's outlay of capital and the size of its industrial empire. Subsequently, demand, too, became inflated. "Having atomic weapons became a status symbol for our services," Arthur Barber, Deputy Assistant Secretary of Defense for International Security Affairs, told me. "The Army wanted to push them into artillery guns, the Navy wanted to pipe them aboard carriers, and the Marines didn't want to have that left-out feeling." In this same connection, James T. Ramey, a member of the Atomic Energy Commission, told me, "What we called the tin-cup theory was then the fashion. The military would come to the Commission and simply say, 'We'll take whatever you're capable of giving us.' "

Tin cups haven't been rattled quite so freely since 1961, when Secretary McNamara took office. Even the Secretary's detractors concede that he is not given to indiscriminate buildups. The standard business practice of evaluating cost effectiveness has been brought to bear heavily on the operations of the Defense Department, and while this may not quite be a redemptive event, it has lent a certain circumspection to the thinking of our military establishment. There are many Pentagon officials, I found, who are quite as well aware as General Kent that the law of diminishing returns isn't easily repealed. "It isn't true, as many people seem to think, that the more weapons we have, the stronger we are," I was told by Alain Enthoven, a former university economics professor who is serving in the Pentagon with the title of Deputy Assistant Secretary of Defense (Systems Analysis). "That's not so, any more than if a man were to go out and spend his money on every pair of shoes in sight. How many of them would he ever get around to wearing? These weapons systems are too damn expensive for us not to ask ourselves whether the next billion we're thinking of spending will do as much as the last billion." I got some idea of just what could be done with one of those billions from Kermit Gordon, Director of the Bureau of the Budget, who was happy that in the fiscal year of 1963 defense costs had been cut by almost precisely that amount. "That billion is a lot bigger in civilian terms than it is in military terms," he said. "With it we can underwrite the anti-poverty program for a year. It's more than the government spends on medical research, and it could make it much easier for us to lay out funds on nurses' education and on the construction of libraries and college classrooms. We could use more of these billions, of course, and perhaps they'll be forthcoming. The Secretary is asking questions that have long been overdue. He is insisting on knowing just what contingencies we are preparing to meet; in other words, he is taking the trouble to relate plans and procurement."

Mr. McNamara's application of the cost-effectiveness principle notwithstanding, our vast industrial complex for producing weapons is a long way from a shutdown. Early in 1964, William C. Foster, director of the United States Arms Control and Disarmament Agency, disclosed at a disarmament conference in Geneva that since 1962 we had tripled our inventory of strategic missiles, and that, unless the concept of enoughness becomes clearer, we shall have more than eight times as many missiles in 1965 as we had in 1962. New production schedules always seem to spring up, as if they followed some immutable law of nature. One justification for increased production was described to me as "humane." This is a variation on the concept of deterrence, and is known as "damage-limiting capability." Its humaneness, in practice, would consist in our aiming our warheads at specific military targets—missile-launching sites, for example—rather than at the enemy's cities. Thus, it was explained to me, densely populated areas would be spared, and at the same time our warheads, by forestalling the dispatch of Communist warheads, would limit damage to this country. The man who gave me this explanation, a highly placed official in the Defense Department, went on to mention that we wouldn't necessarily know it if warheads were being fired at Communist missile silos whose weapons had already been launched or at airfields whose bombers were already en route to our shores, but then, imponderables had to be expected in defense planning. "The important thing to remember about damage-limiting capability is that it's not anti-population but anti-military," he said. "Naturally, it takes fewer weapons just to kill people than to wipe out military targets that are shielded and widely dispersed." (Dr. Brown of the Defense Department informed me, philosophically, "In peace it's called deterrence, and in war it's called damage-limiting capability. One country's capacity for destruction is another's damage-limiting capability.")

Often, I gathered, nothing more than a kind of atmosphere and momentum keeps production rolling. One man who told me about this was a former member of the A.E.C., a veteran of the tin-cup days who left the government a few years ago to resume the practice of law. "Perfectly sensible people would sit around a conference table saying they wanted more and stronger weapons," he recalled. "More targets were constantly being dreamed up. There were times when I thought *individuals* would be named as targets. I myself started out as one of those people whose attitude toward nuclear bombs was the simple, traditional one that they were damned powerful weapons and a good thing to have. I wasn't on the Commission long before I discovered that all that seemed to count was the efficiency of the manufacturing complex we were running—from uranium mines to the finished product. No one ever mentioned what the product was, what it could do. We might have been punching out autos. Eventually, my business instincts were offended. I realized that the Defense Department's budget was—and still is, for that matter—far bigger than is apparent. Thanks to the legal setup, the Defense Department didn't have to pay a cent for the bombs it was insatiably demanding. The A.E.C. was the one that footed the bill. It was then that I began to pay some careful attention to the product, and in doing so I went out to the Pacific for some weapons tests. I stood on an island seventeen miles from where one of those products went off, and felt my skin grabbed and pricked, as though someone had put a match to it—as though it had been exposed to the heat from some new sun. When I got back, I began to ask questions, which was then much less fashionable in the government than it is now, and pretty soon I found that I was no longer going home with the bunch, so to speak—that I was off the circuit."

❦

As I wandered about Washington listening to high government officials, it sometimes crossed my mind that one of the most elusive aspects of the elusive question of enoughness might be whether there was enough wisdom in our own nuclear capital —or in any capital—to resolve the dilemmas that our own ingenuity had called forth. Such doubts were certainly not inspired by any lack of diligence on the part of the officials I met; many of them were putting in twelve-hour days in their offices and doing homework over the weekend besides. Nor did I encounter a shortage of intelligence, or even of intellectuality. Wherever I went, though, I listened to thoughts that were touched with uncertainty and misgiving. This was true even of the statements made by the most ardent proponents of a particular point of view. These men might start out loud and clear, but sooner or later qualification would creep in. Occupied as they were with the daily pressure of duty, they seemed more pragmatic than philosophical in their realization that with nuclear weapons there could be little margin for error. It seemed that only infallibility would do, and, as though that weren't a tall enough order, it had to be achieved before new nuclear countries emerged, as China has been in the process of doing, for such a development, it was made clear to me, was bound to complicate the already complex choices that had to be made. Yet time and again I heard my questions answered with questions. Although high officials unhesitatingly cited the opinions of writers and thinkers who were unburdened by the cares of government, I came to see that within the government itself tentativeness was everywhere, and nothing was a closed book. One man, a scientist who spends his twelve-hour day designing weapons in the Pentagon, wasn't even sure we *should* defend ourselves under any and all circumstances. "I think we should defend ourselves only if we don't give up essential elements of our national life," he told me. The principle of deterrence itself was open to question. Everyone accepted it as our official position now but not necessarily as our permanent one. "I think of deterrence as something to build on," Senator J. William Fulbright, chairman of the Senate Foreign Relations Committee, said to me. "It might lead us to a different policy at some point in the future, but, naturally, we would require solid evidence that it was a better one than what we now have." Another prominent congressional figure felt that the policy of deterrence was gradually losing its good name. "Deterrence is beginning to sound like a blueprint for winning the next war," he said. "Both sides are talking too much about knocking out each other's communications networks and resorting to tactical weapons." Many officials, I found, included among our unresolved dilemmas the disposition of tactical nuclear weapons. Some held that if we opened up a runaway lead over Russia in this department, it would enhance our political influence for a good long time, but others saw different implications. They were concerned lest the use of tactical nuclear weapons in the field lead inevitably to retaliation with strategic, or anti-population, nuclear weapons. Nor were these people happy about the ease with which low-yield weapons were being turned out, to be placed in the hands of military units as small as battalions. "We're on record as opposing proliferation of nuclear weapons among nations, but we're proliferating them among ourselves," a Foreign Service man remarked.

Money was another widespread concern. Many officials raised the question of whether we might conceivably be subverting our economy in the name of the most patriotic of all causes—the nation's defense. If we invested unwisely in the arms race over a long enough period, I was frequently told, we might have to pay dearly in terms of taxes and inflation. We might also have to pay dearly in terms of peacetime international economic competition, for defense production, being for the most part narrow and specialized, could have little application to consumer markets. On this subject, Mr. Barber of the Defense Department once observed at a seminar of the Peace Research Institute, a private Washington organization, "If this trend [of emphasizing defense contracts] continues unabated, in ten years we may have a world monopoly on vehicles that will take us to Venus and Mars, but we may all be driving cars made in Germany, France, and Japan. These nations are putting far more research and development into increasing their commercial efforts than American industry is." The economy was also on the mind of

Lawrence Mirel, a young legislative assistant to Senator George McGovern, of South Dakota, at the time I discussed with him his ideas of enough. "Enough is a function of what *else* you think is important," he said. "Can the military ever have enough money to do what they believe in? No—no more than there could ever be enough teachers and schools to satisfy me. Enough is a matter of weighing national needs against each other—wisely, without catering to one need above all the others."

Among members of Congress, too, I encountered mixed feelings about the money being spent for national defense. One congressman from the Midwest told me that he found it hard to apply ordinary standards of prudence to the defense-appropriation bills that came before him. "It's crisis money they're asking for," he said. "It's like money for an operation—you don't ask questions, you just go ahead and spend it." Senator Pastore had also mentioned difficulties in judging such legislation. "When Mr. McNamara and the Joint Chiefs and the Air Force come up here to the Hill and ask us for fifty billion dollars, there's an expertise demanded of us that isn't easy for laymen," he said. "How do I really know whether or not we need those thousands of bombs that Defense claims we need? And maybe Mr. McNamara, who is no technical man either, is wrong when he tells us he's against the country's having a nuclear aircraft carrier. And how can we tell exactly what's wrapped up in that fifty-billion-dollar defense budget? Maybe it includes some unnecessary office chairs. It all ends up with our having to have trust, the same as the public has to trust us legislators. When we behave like jackasses, I think the public is more hurt than vexed."

Numerous officials assured me that even if we *thought* we had enough weapons, we wouldn't dare really believe it, because there was always the chance that foreign researchers might hit on new kinds of weapons that would render ours obsolete and ineffective. This view may well be equally prevalent in Moscow and other capitals, since it is widely known how busily we ourselves are engaged in "r. and d."—short for "research and development." A good part of our r. and d. is actually concerned with improving the weapons we already have, but its futuristic side has more appeal for our government officials. Many of them, I found, hoped that our scientists and engineers might come up with a weapon at once so novel and so decisive that it would, in effect, restore the political power we had during our years of nuclear monopoly. (Presumably, we would use the power differently.) But with r. and d., as with other aspects of defense, there were officials who discerned a basic dilemma. Innovation had always begotten innovation, these people said, and went on to argue that r. and d. might well amount to little more than a technological egging on of the arms race. "If you let it, r. and d. can lead you straight into fantasy," one official told me. "Why, just the other day I heard of some Air Force people who are itching for space weapons with which to fight battles back of the moon."

Many r.-and-d. projects definitely in the works

have an aura of fantasy. Among them, according to statements given out by the House Armed Services Committee, are a death-ray type of weapon that may be evolved from laser research, chemical and biological agents that can temporarily incapacitate human beings, space platforms for the launching of weapons, and orbiting missiles that can be made to strike targets on command. The possibility of an anti-missile missile is also, of course, widely mentioned, but there is no general agreement that it would prove a hundred per cent effective as a defensive weapon, which is probably the only standard that matters. Its responses, it has been suggested, might well be thrown out of whack by decoys or by bombs fitted with multiple warheads. Moreover, I was told that sheer numbers of missiles could overtax the responses of anti-missile missiles—a possibility that clearly would call for a sharp increase in weapons production. One man I talked with—a researcher with the A.E.C.—wasn't sure that even a foolproof anti-missile missile would be useful. "Suppose that an enemy missile heading for Detroit is intercepted just as it crosses high over Cleveland," he said. "Well, Detroit will come out all right, but there will be one hell of an explosion in Cleveland."

The two men directly in charge of r. and d. for the Defense Department—Dr. Brown and his deputy, Dr. Eugene Fubini—attributed no special mystique to their domain, saying that whatever unusual ingenuity was involved had to be closely tied to the needs of the political world. "There are very few technological facts that cannot be explained to intelligent laymen," Dr. Fubini told me. "R.-and-d. men simply try to present a kind of gross geometry for the consideration of those responsible for particular decisions. If the deployment of a particular type of weapon is being considered, we show different frameworks in which this may be accomplished, each framework having its own set of details, such as costs and effects. If one framework doesn't suit, then another is presented. That's the basis on which r. and d. has always operated—as far back as the bow and arrow. The musket, you know, didn't succeed the bow and arrow because it was technologically superior. Those first muskets were dreadful, as a matter of fact. They were far less accurate than the bow and arrow, but the bow and arrow, you see, had priced themselves out of the weapons market. The cost of making arrows and of training archers had got way out of line." As for Dr. Brown, he felt that we had to go ahead with our r. and d. as long as the Communists went ahead with theirs. We simply couldn't afford to be sloppy, and hence vulnerable, he said; nuclear war might well be unthinkable but that wouldn't make it impossible. "It's too bad that this is a two-man game," he went on, referring to our r.-and-d. contest with the Communists. "But the game is growing older, and someone, I suppose, might argue that it's a good thing—that the more weapons systems the two sides devise, the fewer surprises there can possibly be in store."

The need for wisdom, it was pointed out to me in the course of my inquiry, is compounded by the curious possibility that the United States and the

Soviet Union may be in arms races with themselves as well as with each other. This possibility, which adds immeasurably to the elusiveness of the question of enough, derives from the fact that the arms race is by no means the symmetrical affair that it is commonly supposed to be. We and the Russians, it appears, do not match new weapon for new weapon, production schedule for production schedule. In the period when we were building up our fleet of B-52 bombers, for example, the Russians were concentrating on missiles, and when the Russians were preoccupied with submarines, we were busy expanding our ground forces. Moreover, according to Defense Department people who have dealt with the Russians, their nation and ours don't even go about assessing the respective threats to themselves in the same way. "We don't believe a nuclear war would last long, but they seem to think in terms of campaigning through one," I was told by one of Secretary McNamara's chief assistants. "They envision a devastating beginning for both sides and then a war that would go on and on until the Americans finally learned the same lesson that Napoleon and the Nazis did—that Mother Russia's sons, and her winters, and her geographical vastness are unconquerable."

The upshot of this asymmetry, I gathered, is that to a considerable extent there may now be in progress two unilateral races that bear little relation to each other or to the main one that we are constantly hearing about. These races, clearly, would not be going on if each side knew what the other was up to, but until such a day dawns, the Pentagon and its

Soviet counterpart will be understandably preoccupied with perfecting what they do know about for certain: their own military establishments. "If we had no guessing to do about Russia's plans, there would be no problem of enough," one of our leading military researchers told me. "There will always be a need for some weapons, in my opinion, but if we knew there would be no thermonuclear war, would we need to deploy as many missiles as we have? And, conversely, if we knew there *would* be a war, wouldn't we damn well be doing even more than we are? In other words, what I am saying to you is that decisions are being made today on the basis of incomplete information."

Some of the guesswork that currently guides governments is being eliminated by means of inventions like the so-called spy satellites now in orbit over both Russian and American territory, but potentially, according to various officials, the great breakthrough in mutual intelligence could come through treaties that effectively limit the production of weapons and control their possible use; if agreements of this sort should ever be reached, then international inspection of defense plants, laboratories, missile bases, airfields, and the like would become automatic and routine. Until that occurs, though, "we're in the catastrophe business," as one official put it. "Quite simply, there are two approaches to security: through arms and through arms control," I was told by Adam Yarmolinsky, Special Assistant to the Secretary of Defense. The arms-control approach has never been tried, of course, and its unfamiliarity, I found, seemed to impose upon some officials the need for exerting a nuclear wisdom, so to speak, as opposed to the conventional variety. A number of them appeared to look upon arms control with an instinctive mistrust, denouncing it as colossal naïveté or a colossal swindle or both. It conjured up for them the spectre of politicians' capitulating to "peace demands" from the multitude. "Disarmament isn't some vague, wishful evangelism," a career man in the State Department told me. "If it ever comes, it will be the culmination of a long series of delicate political settlements."

Reservations about arms control are, of course, not a purely American phenomenon. Many of the governments that are accustomed to our protection, I was told, fear that arms control might lead to the withdrawal of that protection. (In fact, I was frequently informed that probably the only country as keenly interested in disarmament as we are is the Soviet Union.) Nor are our sister nations above a hypocritical maneuver or two when it comes to the ideal of disarmament. A member of the House Foreign Affairs Committee recalled that back in 1961, at the very moment the United Nations General Assembly was unanimously passing a resolution calling for worldwide disarmament, seventy of the voting nations were dickering with the United States for military aid. And in 1963, Secretary Rusk told me, when the relations between Russia and this country were in one of their more benign phases, he was sounded out on the subject by a European Foreign Minister as the two men were leaving a conference table abroad. "The Foreign Minister apparently had rosy hopes for the future," the Secretary told me. "As we walked out together, he said, 'If you and the Russians sign a disarmament treaty, would you give us a good price on some of the weapons you're getting rid of?' "

Skeptical or not, practically everyone I saw recognized in arms limitation a potential method of relaxing the present military standoff. One senator was for it because he thought we were too trustful in our attitude toward the Communists. "Every day the sun comes up, we're letting them decide whether they feel like being deterred or not," he said to me. "If we or some international inspection commission could get in there, we could tell for sure what they had in mind." The more I discussed arms control with government officials, the more it seemed to me that no sharp line divided the "doves" from the "hawks." It was certainly not a case of their being in harmonious agreement without knowing it, but they did have a bond in the seriousness with which they approached the subject of arms control. When I remarked on this to Dr. Herbert Scoville, Jr., Assistant Director for Science and Technology of the Arms Control and Disarmament Agency, he nodded, and cited as supporting evidence his own government career. "I was with the Defense Department, then I went over to the Central Intelligence Agency, and now here I am with the Arms Control and Disarmament Agency," he said. His present boss, William C. Foster, the director of the A.C.D.A., previously served as Deputy Secretary of Defense.

The absence of a sharp dividing line was evident

everywhere, especially in the last place where many people would expect this to be true—in the Pentagon. The various military services there, I heard, were all sponsoring arms-control studies of varying sorts; even the Joint Chiefs of Staff, the very heart of American militarism, were doing so. "We're used to dealing in weapons in this building. We can fire them for you or control them," I was told by a Navy captain whose chest was awash with decorations from the last war. Paeans to relaxing the arms race were almost suspiciously easy to come by, but I did hear of a number of specific steps that had been taken toward this end. One of them is the disclosure, since 1961, of fairly complete data concerning our arsenal of missiles, bombers, submarines, and the rest. By advertising our strength in some detail, our policy-makers reason, we may help to discourage any rash enterprise on the part of a potential enemy. "It's a new conception of security," a Defense Department official told me. "Security used to be regarded as synonymous with secrecy, but now it's being turned into a form of open communication. The President himself has coöperated in this, even telling the world, in an address to the U.S. Coast Guard Academy, the number of special-action teams we have trained to combat subversive activities abroad."

Paradoxical though it may seem, the goal of restraining the arms race is taken into account even in the designing of our weapons. Some types of arms, it appears, convey a more menacing impression abroad than others do, equally devastating though they may all be. Consequently, Defense Department technicians seek to devise weapons that they consider "unprovocative." A Polaris missile, whose yield is fifty times that of the Hiroshima bomb, is considered a model of tact, I was informed, because it lends itself to both mobility and concealment. "It's as much out of sight under those waves as though we had general and complete disarmament," a young weapons designer told me. "But that Jupiter missile! It's been phased out for two years now, but that sure was a provocative weapon. It gives me the willies to think we ever deployed it over in Turkey and Italy. It practically screamed that it had no place to go but Russia. It sat out in the open for everyone to see—sleek and erect aboveground, with armed troops guarding it. And it was so vulnerable! I mean, its skin was so thin you could probably shred it with a couple of bullets. All you needed for an anti-missile missile back in those days was a rifle."

Very soon, I was told, all our strategic missiles will be out of sight, deep in underground silos, whose cylindrical walls are hardened with tons of concrete. Far from being vulnerable, these buried missiles are all certified as "survivable"—capable of withstanding a one-megaton shot less than a mile away. While survivability naturally has its military implications, I was told that it is also a formidable political achievement, for if an enemy knows he is up against invulnerable weapons, he is unlikely to be tempted into taking any rash action; in short, it is theorized that the stability of weapons and the stability of the arms race are as one. "Our gain in security doesn't necessarily imply a concomitant Soviet loss," a Defense Department official told me. "That is the great distinction of all arms-control measures that aren't phony. They make for a mutual security. And if the Russians achieve survivability of their strategic missiles, which might be in the next few years, the arms race may be further stabilized."

❦

Despite these halting steps toward mutual security, it is secrecy about military and political strategy that remains the general rule, and it is deterrence—the great alternative to arms control—that remains our fixed policy, as it may for years to come. Its fortunes record now moments of high jeopardy, now phases of almost millennial promise, these rises and falls all being traceable to the fear we share with the Communists; namely, the fear of the daily possibility of a surprise attack. Neither side, I was assured over and over, has any wish to initiate such an attack, but both are deeply aware that an accident may upset their plans. Our own officials are haunted by the thought that we may all be ambushed by error, human or mechanical, Soviet or American. They are in almost continuous conclave about this, I learned, their sessions being devoted to imagining what could possibly go wrong, since they know that in the absence of a deliberate attack the policy of deterrence depends for its efficiency on their imagination. Fortunately, we are not alone in grasping this point. One of our highest officials, a man who sees top-secret intelligence reports, told me, "The Russians are storing their weapons carefully. And they, too, are taking care that only their most responsible people retain control over those weapons."

The same official doubted, however, whether the Communists' caution quite matched our own, and as I listened to him and to colleagues of his, I could not help being impressed by the meticulous efforts we are making to forestall mishaps. The construction of our bombs is a case in point. They are fitted out with all manner of safeguards. A bomb, I was told, will not go off accidentally even if it is dropped from an airplane, consumed by a fire, or struck by lightning. At most, its non-nuclear high-explosive section—its priming fuse, so to speak—might go off, but that would produce only a high-explosive blast. The nuclear warhead, it seems, can be activated only if "several things" happen in proper sequence, after which a set of electrical signals have to be flashed in a certain pattern with precise timing. Even then, I was told, a weapon will still not be activated until it has passed through various environmental changes involving velocity and barometric pressures. A special switch for arming the weapon can be tampered with only if the weapon is disassembled—and therefore disarmed. As another form of safeguard, nuclear-weapons designers sometimes deliberately omit automated gadgetry from their creations, to keep them from being fired too easily. For example, I was told by John T. McNaughton, Assistant Secretary of Defense for International Security Affairs, that one of the most important steps in the launching of a certain kind of missile, the process of providing the launching mechanism with its critical power supply, is performed in a fashion that might make an onlooker think he was down on the farm. "When the signal for that step is given," McNaughton said, "a man standing in a distant corner starts turning a hand crank that looks just like the one on an old-fashioned ice-cream freezer." As for the arming of such a weapon, the various steps necessary have been made too numerous and too complex for any one man to handle. This also applies, McNaughton said, to preparing a one-man fighter-bomber for takeoff with nuclear armaments. "The pilot would have to be an octopus with a twenty-foot reach to be able to do it all by himself," he went on. "And even if he were able to, he couldn't take off without proper authorization. If he tried it, he'd find his plane's runway blocked by barricades on the airfield. They're always in place to provide against the possibility of anyone's trying a stunt like that."

Such acts of individual impulsiveness, it was emphasized to me by numerous Defense Department officials, were possible only in movies and novels, and my informants displayed a distinct touchiness about plots that involved pilots zooming off on self-authorized bombing missions. "Positive control," as it was called, was exercised at all times, I was told. Thus, no Strategic Air Command pilot was permitted to fly beyond a predetermined point without an explicit "go" order, which had to come from the highest authority and could not be sent out by mistake, as novelists have suggested. I gathered, though, that this was an administrative rather than a physical restraint—and that, as an official put it, was "the difference between 'may' and 'can.'" One Defense Department man did concede that, through what he described as "a fantastic combination of extremely unlikely possibilities," the crash of an S.A.C. plane could result in an accidental nuclear explosion. The odds against it were enormous, he emphasized, but he did reluctantly contemplate the possibility. "What if the plane crashed on an American city?" he asked. "We wouldn't know who or what had hit us. Until we investigated, we wouldn't know whether there had been a crash or an attack. And in a few years the investigation might be truly complicated if new nuclear powers had entered the arms race."

One important safeguard on nuclear missiles consists of "permissive-action links" (known, cozily and inevitably, as PAL), which are electro-mechanical locks that only American officers in possession of a special code can unlock. The inspiration for PAL was itself a sort of accident, I learned from Commissioner Ramey of the A.E.C. Ramey, who was formerly the executive director of the Joint Congressional Committee on Atomic Energy, told me that the PAL system was largely the by-product of an inspection tour of missile bases in NATO countries that he and members of the committee made in 1960. "We were scared stiff by what we saw," he recalled. As the group looked over the bases, he said, they became increasingly worried by the infringement of our national sovereignty, since it was apparent that we didn't necessarily retain control of our own weapons when they were in foreign territory. "It was always the same, whether we were in Britain or in Turkey," Ramey went on. "The ally on whose soil the base was situated owned the delivery vehicle but not its warhead. That belonged to us. If the missile ever had to be launched, a so-called two-key arrangement was supposed to go into effect, which meant that an officer of ours and, say, his Turkish counterpart each had a special key of his own, which was to be inserted in the proper place. When that was done, the weapon would become operational. But we wondered what would happen if, for some reason—two NATO allies falling out, perhaps—the Turk decided to overpower our man and take away his key? Why, the Turk would have himself quite a modern weapon, that's what. It wasn't long after we returned home that PAL was figured out."

Important though PAL and other such safeguards may be, they are only one aspect of the government's concern that, come what may, in war or peace, the command and control of our men and arms be preserved within the bounds of orderly, Constitutional authority. It is the inordinate power of modern weapons, I was told, that has made something special of "command and control," as officials now refer to this once routine matter. A governmental committee has met dozens of times to figure out ways of preventing an accident from irretrievably harming our form of government, and a number of these meetings have been attended by the President himself. "There wouldn't be much sense in defending ourselves if we neglected to preserve the Constitution," I was told by Deputy Secretary Cyrus R. Vance, a forthright, thoughtful lawyer who is the second-highest member of the Defense Department, and who has spent many long hours pondering the intricacies of command and control. Under the law, Vance informed me, the President, and the President alone, controls the detonation of American nuclear weapons, even for peacetime testing. Once the President has decided that such an event may take place, his order makes its way down the long chain of command that ends with the man on the firing line. This arrangement appears manageable enough at present, but in a time of nuclear crisis unexpected contingencies might come thick and fast. It is the possibility of such contingencies, I gathered, that has provoked the thoughts and speculations of the committee considering command and control, nearly all of which have to do with insuring that we are never without the services of a President. "The President's survivability is crucial to our way of life," a member of the committee told me. "As our highest elected official, he normally goes a long way toward standing for the popular will. If we were attacked, that might be more true than ever, because it might be impossible to convene Congress."

This official didn't discuss the committee's conclusions, if any, but he did give me an idea of the sort of question it dealt with. One example had to do with just who should be with the President in the event of a severe crisis. The President might have to operate out of a relatively cramped refuge at a time like that, and this would seriously limit the size of his emergency staff. His Secretaries of State and Defense and the

Joint Chiefs were obvious choices, but who else? Wouldn't the chairman of the Atomic Energy Commission have important opinions about fallout conditions? What about the President's family and his trusted personal advisers? Whoever finally made up the group, what would it have to decide? Incoming reports about the developing situation would determine that, and these reports, in turn, would depend on the President's communications setup. In view of his cramped quarters, it was a question whether it would be realistic to provide him with, for instance, a large display board, like the one at the Strategic Air Command Headquarters at Omaha, which, among other things, can show planes and missiles en route to their targets. And whatever the size of the board, what kind of information, in general, would it make most sense for the President to receive? That was the vital question, the committee member said, since it might determine whether the President ordered a controlled or a spasmodic response to enemy action. Computer data would help the President reach that decision, and this raised the question of what type of computer would do the job best, and with what other computers the Presidential computer would have to be able to communicate if he were to receive adequate data. Since the survivability of the President could not be guaranteed, arrangements would have to be made for the Vice-President's safety, my informant went on, but should our second in command be included among the people who were with the President or should he proceed to an alternate headquarters of his own? As for the President's emergency quarters, the site was another debatable matter. In the past, the consensus had been that it should definitely not be in the vicinity of Washington, but second thoughts are now being had on that score. There were people who doubted if the President would have enough time to get very far from the White House, regardless of whether we were faced with a tactical or a strategic warning—that is, with the prospect of an imminent attack or the prospect of an attack within days or weeks. If a tactical warning came in, the President would only have between fifteen and thirty minutes in which to make his exit. But even if an attack on Washington and other American cities were threatened for weeks, the President would still be strapped for time, because those very weeks might represent a last chance for us and our adversary to come to some sort of understanding. "It might not behoove the President to make for the hills at a time like that," the official said. "It might create panic at home, and as for the reaction abroad, his departure would very quickly be interpreted there as either a sign of weakness or a preparation for the launching of an American attack."

The President's role as capstone of our system of command and control is possibly his most difficult one, it was emphasized by McGeorge Bundy, the Special Assistant for National Security Affairs to Presidents Kennedy and Johnson. Each morning, Bundy told me, the President wakes up to the uneasy knowledge that he has the power to order a nuclear bombing. "A President may not know the exact pressure measurements of this or that weapon, the way scientists do, but he knows something they don't—the way it feels to be the one man who is able to direct that those weapons be used," Bundy said. "He lives with that knowledge, and he must regard it with the utmost gravity. President Kennedy, I remember, once said to me that he would consider it 'the ultimate failure' if he ever saw fit to use a nuclear weapon. I have the impression that President Johnson feels the same way. I think of them both as men with an enormous desire for historical success."

Apart from the exercise of poor political judgment, the chances of a President's causing an accident are probably remote; he is surrounded by too many advisers and bodyguards for his actions to be governed by such ordinary lapses as forgetfulness, inattention, or fatigue, or by the quirks of personality to which everyone, including Russians, is subject. But a President's military subordinates—hundreds of thousands of disciplined men in uniform operating within the framework of command and control—are another matter. It was freely admitted to me that, explicit though their orders may be, there is never any telling, as all these great numbers of individuals go about their daily duties, when one of them will step out of line for reasons that may not be known even to himself. The possibility of such missteps, I learned, has prompted the Defense Department to organize what is called the Human Reliability Program, a vast undertaking that, as far as I can make out, is dedicated to the proposition that no one in our armed forces may take leave of his senses and let fly with a nuclear weapon. "Twenty-four hours a day, three hundred and sixty-five days a year, I'm concerned with the maturity and stability of every man under my command," I was told by Colonel Richard R. Stewart, commander of the 820th Strategic Aerospace Division, at Plattsburgh, in upstate New York, where both bombers and intercontinental ballistic missiles are held ready for action. "Twenty-three years ago, when I was at my first airbase, my C.O. didn't need to think that way. When I reported to him as a second lieutenant, he said to me, 'From eight in the morning to five in the afternoon, what you do is my business, but after the flag comes down, it's strictly your own.' "

Most of my information about the Human Reliability Program came from the two men who head it—Walter T. Skallerup, Jr., a civilian, and Colonel Paul M. Richards, of the Air Force—both of whom, I thought, had a very reliable manner. They eventually referred me to a psychiatrist, but before they did, I learned that the program has been functioning since 1962 and that the need for it was underscored by a security violation whose peculiar aspects had aroused the interest of both the Defense Department and the Joint Congressional Committee on Atomic Energy. (Details of the violation remain classified.) Even before the Defense Department embarked on its Human Reliability Program, the Air Force had been looking into manifestations of abnormal psychology within its nuclear ranks. Its studies, I was told, were at least partly inspired by an incident in which General LeMay himself had figured, along with an enlisted man assigned to guard the General's parked plane. The incident, Colonel Richards recalled, took place in 1960 at Strategic Air Command Headquarters. "As the General approached his plane, he noticed that someone's initials had been crudely carved on the door of the plane," the Colonel said. "That wasn't much in itself, but it was obvious that anyone who was capable of doing that might have also done something more serious to the plane. Anyway, investigators found that the initials were the guard's, and that he'd scratched them with his penknife."

The Human Reliability Program has since collected other examples of curious behavior, a number of which Skallerup described to me matter-of-factly. "Sometimes Air Police get bored with guard duty and shoot at each other," he said. "Or maybe a guard is spooked by shadows and by his fear of Communists. We once received a report of a sabotage attempt when rocks were found inside a bomber's jet intake. Investigators traced them to a guard who had hit his head on the plane and had decided to get even by heaving rocks at it."

Colonel Richards observed that occasionally men in more responsible posts tended to become prey to unusual strains of conscience while on the job. "They get disturbed about the consequences of using the weapons to which they've been assigned," he said. "It impairs their motivation. There's a man who's flying a transport right now for that reason. He had to be reassigned from an ICBM silo, and I understand that until he started having doubts about what he was doing, he appeared as happy and integrated as a man could be."

Life in a silo was not easy, Skallerup said, and went on, "It's a little like being locked up in a bank vault. Those silos are a hundred feet or so deep, and they probably seem deeper to someone who thought he was joining the Air Force to roam the wild blue yonder. And even if a fellow does draw flying duty, it's drilled into him that things aren't the way they used to be back in the days when a hot pilot was a guy who would grab himself a couple of Scotches and go. He has to be even-tempered and responsible at all times." Various measures are employed to counter the dangers of non-combat fatigue. The political lesson of armed restraint—of deterrence, that is—is taught and retaught, its theme being summed up in S.A.C.'s well-known motto: "Peace Is Our Profession." Air crews are constantly put through combat alerts, the men spilling out of ready shacks to get their planes off the ground in less than fifteen minutes. Missile teams, huddled in their vaults beneath the rural landscape, are frequently rehearsed in countdowns and in the dangerous process of fuelling their weapons with liquid propellants. The Human Reliability Program, Skallerup told me, covers all men who have "the knowledge and opportunity" to make trouble at nuclear stations. "Emotional checks," as he put it, have been run on a quarter of a million men in the Air Force alone. Of that number, thousands were judged to need clinical evaluation, and of those a significant number were transferred from nuclear duty. The medical records of men on nuclear duty carry special tabs, to alert the examining physician when they report for sick call. If they should betray any sign of instability, the physician is required to make this known to their commanding officer, so that they can be counselled or assisted in an effort to save them for nuclear duty. "It's a delicate balance that we're trying to strike," Skallerup said. "We want the men stable but not phlegmatic. We don't want to hurt their spirit, yet we have to keep them toeing the line."

The psychiatrist to whom Skallerup and Richards referred me was Dr. Eugene R. Inwood, a former Army medical officer who is professor of psychiatry at Georgetown University School of Medicine and who has been associated with the Human Reliability Program since its inception. Dr. Inwood, who received me in the study of his home, outside the capital, provided me with further instances of the wayward nature of even carefully checked, highly trained military technicians. The individual vagaries uncovered had prompted the wider application of a "two-man rule," he told me, whereby officers and technicians on certain duty were under orders to move in pairs when they were in what are called "no-lone zones." The idea back of the arrangement, the Doctor said, was to enable each man to make sure that his sidekick wasn't up to anything aberrational. Guards were assigned to enforce the "two-man rule," and the guards, too, had to move in pairs. "There's no question but that technical people and officers whose training or authority is above a certain level can do substantial damage," Dr. Inwood said. "That doesn't hold for maintenance people, though some of them are in a position to set off explosives that are not nuclear in origin." He added that full colonels and some generals now come under the purview of the

Human Reliability Program, which didn't use to cover officers of such rank; they had been included only after protracted urging by the Doctor himself and other psychiatrists, and, climactically, the accidental discovery that an S.A.C. colonel was an alcoholic. Dr. Inwood could recall other instances of alarming conduct—conduct of a sort that, he said, could be expected in any large military organization regardless of nationality. An American sergeant stationed in England had pulled his .45 and threatened to shoot at a nuclear bomb. A technical sergeant holding down an important job in New Mexico had been driven to distraction by a nervous wife and had been reassigned just in time. A technical sergeant at one of our bases in Spain had come to the end of his rope after ten years of nuclear duty, but hadn't asked to be relieved, for fear it might hurt his career; he had refused to answer the phone and had behaved so oddly in other respects that the men under him had finally petitioned a flight surgeon to examine their superior. "The sergeant is running a motor pool now," Dr. Inwood told me, and added, "We try to do the best we can, but if each of us were capable of rational behavior at all times, would there have ever been any need for nuclear weapons to be invented?"

❦

The entrance to an ICBM silo—or, to give its official designation, launch-control center—is called an "entrapment area," and it is accurately named, as I know from having stood inside one on a day I visited an underground Atlas. The entrapment area was a hollow cubicle of darkness, ten feet long, five feet wide, and eight feet high. The steel door through which I had entered it, with a military escort, had closed behind me. Before me was another steel door leading to the interior. In a corner of the ceiling was a closed-circuit television camera, through which the invisible commanding officer of the missile team within the silo peered at me and my escort as he challenged us, in a sepulchral voice. My companion, responding earnestly, identified us and stated our business; his name was Captain Richard W. Wetzel, and he was ordinarily a silo commander himself. Neither Wetzel's voice nor presence, I found, did much to mitigate my sense of entrapment, and I tried to remember the landscape I had just blotted out for myself. I was a mile from the Canadian border, in a corner of upstate New York above Plattsburgh that was in the nuclear domain of Colonel Stewart, and the countryside there was sunny and verdant with maples and birches. Herds of Jerseys were grazing in a nearby pasture, the property of a dairy farmer who had chosen to sell the Air Force an acre of his land for this emplacement. Now, in the entrapment area, I recalled the sign at the gate leading into the militarized acre: "It is unlawful to enter this area without authority of the Base Commander. . . . Area is patrolled by armed guards and vicious sentry dogs."

"Fuel!" Wetzel told the television camera, giving the day's password.

The door before us was pulled open, but there were two more steel doors to go—mammoth ones, weighing a half ton each. They were blastproof, and had been designed to protect the ICBM from earthquakes and near misses. Each door was opened only long enough to admit us, and then secured again. When we were past both of them, I found myself looking at a lounge and galley, whose stores, I was told, included a ten days' supply of emergency rations. (The silo, which had taken two years to build and cost ten million dollars, had its own water and power supply.) I followed Wetzel down a short flight of stairs to the silo's headquarters room—an area, about thirty by forty feet, that put me in mind of a hospital operating theatre, possibly because fluorescent lamps glared brilliantly against its pastel walls. The room was crammed with instrumentation, the most prominent piece of equipment being a large console covered with twinkling green, red, and amber lights. Through windows I could see two small rooms, one containing double-decker beds and the other a library of technical manuals stamped "SECRET." The silo's commanding officer was in the headquarters room as I entered. He was sitting in an easy chair watching television, a revolver strapped at his side. The image on the screen before him was that of his own ICBM warhead, and he was viewing it in order to make sure that it wasn't afire or being tampered with. "Channel One," he said, taking a last look at the picture before he rose to greet Wetzel and me. He introduced himself as Major Robert Carr. The officers stood side by side for a moment, two nice-looking, cheerful men in their thirties, Carr blond and Wetzel brown-haired. The working uniforms worn by Carr and his men, several of whom were on duty in the headquarters room, added to the hospital atmosphere. They wore impeccable white coveralls, designed to show up any stains made by hazardous chemicals. "An ICBM silo is a spotless place," Carr remarked to me.

Before we left him to inspect the missile, he relieved us of our wristwatches; their straps, he explained, might snag on a piece of equipment or their movements might be damaged by a vagrant high-voltage current. In exchange, he gave us hard hats, and Wetzel and I clambered through a low fifty-foot tunnel that was closed off at each end by two more blastproof doors. The tunnel led to the vertical shaft that held the ICBM, and we were scarcely there when a young technical sergeant in white coveralls joined us unobtrusively. We were standing on a narrow ledge whose walls were stencilled "NO-LONE ZONE." Below us were other levels, and below them were the base of the silo and the missile's launching platform. One could descend into the silo by means of a spiral staircase or by means of an elevator that sounded a clanging, ambulancelike bell when it was in use. Around us were phones, fire alarms, fire-fighting equipment, oxygen masks, and emergency flashlights. Lining the cylindrical chamber were four sets of the most immense springs I have ever seen, their huge coils of steel extending down four levels below; they were designed to help absorb the shock of an earthquake or a near miss by an enemy weapon. The missile itself, at the center of the silo, was sheathed in an encircling wall of steel, called the crib, which was broken by apertures through which one could see the graceful stainless-steel body of the Atlas, eighty-four feet tall. My eye went to the warhead. It wasn't sharp-nosed, as I had expected, but blunt, and it had been painted a drab grayish-white.

"I can't tell you its yield or its target," Wetzel volunteered.

"Is it loaded?" I asked.

He replied pleasantly. "We're on alert, and that weapon cost a million dollars."

We descended the steep, winding staircase to the next level, which, except for glimpses of the ever-present Atlas through the apertures, was solid with panels of contacts and relays. These were crucial in governing the sequence of the missile's actions, Wetzel told me, and I could deduce their importance for myself by the open suspicion with which the sergeant eyed me. There was a constant loud, whirring noise, which Wetzel said was the sound of air being washed in a dust collector. The silo, Wetzel said, depended heavily on water; it was needed for air-conditioning, for cooling diesel generators, and for fighting the fires that might be started by diesel fumes and other hazards. As we walked to the elevator to make our next descent, Wetzel, hospitably making talk, spoke of his plans for his eventual retirement. He hadn't yet decided how to spend it, he said, sounding as though his missile days were already behind him. He rather looked forward to a second career, he went on—not that he regretted for one minute the years he had put in with the Air Force. "It's been a good way of life," he said. "I may go into animal husbandry. I majored in that at Penn State, and it's been of some use to me in my work with missiles. It helped bring out my mechanical skills, and it taught me about chemicals."

The elevator was freight-size and slow-moving, and we spent each of our downward rides listening to its clanging bell. A new sound, deep and thumping, took over as we approached Level 6, and Wetzel showed me where it was coming from—a gray diesel generator squatting massively in a corner. As we continued our inspection, I saw many other things: bottles of helium; small brass pipes, which detected noxious gases in the atmosphere; air-support cylinders, whose function, like that of the enormous springs above, was to help maintain the missile's balance in the event of violent earth shocks; emergency showers, for washing burns that the men might suffer in changing the silo's exotic fuels; and emergency eye showers—basins specially fitted out with spouts for cleansing eyes burned by acids. Here, also, was a large white cylindrical tank containing twenty-three thousand gallons of LOX (liquid oxygen), the missile's primary fuel, whose normal temperature is —297° F. "Plenty of fire in there," he said. "But when we fuel up, the LOX-loading lines get so cold you can't even tap them without injuring your finger."

Eventually, the three of us stood at the very base of the silo, well below the missile's tail. The launching platform was there—a rectangular gray metal slab—and, unaccountably, the sight of it brought back to me one of Blake's "Proverbs of Hell": "You never know what is enough unless you know what is more than enough." Our view of the Atlas was now unimpeded, the bottom of its encircling wall being ten or fifteen feet above us. I looked up toward the warhead, but it was obscured by the missile's gleaming bulk. I wondered whether the birches and dairy herds were still visible in the outdoors above, and looked at my wrist to check the time, only to be reminded that Major Carr had my watch. Wetzel smiled. "Relax," he said easily. "There's nothing to do down here but wait and hope for nothing to happen."

Index

About the Author

Daniel Lang is a graduate of the University of Wisconsin, where he majored in sociology. After an assortment of jobs in scattered parts of the country, he found one as a reporter on the *New York Post*. It was then that he started writing articles for *The New Yorker,* joining its staff in 1942. He was sent overseas shortly thereafter as a war correspondent, witnessing the liberation of much of Italy and southern France. *An Inquiry into Enoughness* is Mr. Lang's fourth book dealing with the social impact of science and technology. He does not seek to dispense technical knowledge. As one reviewer has said, "Daniel Lang is a writer, not a science writer, a literary stylist whose eye is fixed on history and mortal man." Eric Sevareid has described his stories as being concerned with "the human ecology of the atom" and the late historian Carl Van Doren termed him "the Bulfinch of the sudden new mythology" created by the atomic age. The foreword to his first book, *Early Tales of the Atomic Age,* was written by Albert Einstein. Mr. Lang's work has been translated into many languages, including Japanese, Hindi, Arabic and Russian. His last book, *From Hiroshima to the Moon,* was a choice of the Library of Science book club. He has also written short stories, poetry, and a children's book. He is married and has three daughters.